LIVING WITH MENTAL ILLNESS

HUMAN HORIZONS SERIES

LIVING WITH MENTAL ILLNESS

A Book for Relatives and Friends

ELIZABETH KUIPERS, BSc, MSc, PhD, FBPSS
PAUL BEBBINGTON, MA, PhD, FRCP, FRCPsych

A CONDOR BOOK
SOUVENIR PRESS (E&A) LTD

First published 1987 by Souvenir Press (Educational & Academic) Ltd,
43 Great Russell Street, London WC1B 3PA
and simultaneously in Canada

Reprinted 1989
Second edition, completely revised, enlarged and reset, 1997

ISBN 0 285 63349 X

Typeset by Rowland Phototypesetting Ltd
Bury St Edmunds, Suffolk
Printed and bound in Great Britain by
The Guernsey Press Co. Ltd, Guernsey, Channel Islands

Contents

Foreword to the First Edition viii
Preface to the Second Edition ix
Authors' Acknowledgements x
Introduction 1
1 **Mental Illness** 5
Experiencing a severe mental illness 7
Causes 15
Symptoms 20
Outlook 29
2 **Coping with Mental Illness** 31
The problems you may have to deal with 31
After-effects of the illness 32
Unacceptable or embarrassing behaviour 34
Coping with a depressed relative 35
Coping with delusions 38
Restlessness, overactivity and anxiety 40
Effects on sexual relationships 40
Promiscuity as a problem 41
Diet 42
Self-care 43
Use of alcohol 44
Substance abuse 45
Suicide threats 45
Dealing with emergencies 46
Coping with violent behaviour 52
Money problems 56
What can be done if your relative cannot manage his or her affairs because of mental illness? 57
Children in the family 58
Relapse 60

3 **Community Care in the 1990s** 63
Policy changes since 1985 63
The Care Programme Approach 65
The purchaser/provider split and the role of the GP 67
The specialist psychiatric services 68
Mental health clients and the courts 69
Involving relatives and friends 69
The protection of information 70
Supervision Registers 72
4 **Services** 74
The people involved in the care of your relative 74
The services available to your relative 81
Dealing with mental health professionals 88
Second opinions 92
Other sources of support 93
5 **Treatment** 95
Admission to hospital 95
'Physical' treatment 96
Drugs in mental illness 96
Problems with taking medication 111
ECT (electroconvulsive therapy) 112
Psychosurgery 114
Social and psychological treatments 115
Occupational therapy 116
Sheltered workshops 117
Group meetings 118
Individual treatments 119
Family sessions 121
Relatives' groups 122
Alternative medicine and psychiatry 123
6 **Legal Matters** 124
The rights of clients and relatives 124
The rights of voluntary clients 125
The client's nearest relative 125
Who can be admitted or detained against their will? 126
Admission and detention unter the Mental Health Act 1983 127
Safeguards following a compulsory admission 129
Compulsory treatment 134
Clients' mail 136

Complaining about treatment or the use of compulsory powers 136
Wills and contracts 137
Other rights and duties 138
7 **Looking After Yourself** 140
Holidays 144
The future 144
Getting further advice and information 145
Appendix 1: Getting around the Benefit System 147
Appendix 2: Useful Addresses 155
Index 176

Foreword to the First Edition

This book was written in memory of two members of our family who suffered from mental illness. Our experiences with them made us appreciate the need for something specially written for those confronted by mental illness in someone close to them. We put the idea to the Mental Health Foundation, who asked Dr Kuipers and Dr Bebbington to write this book. We hope that the result of their enthusiasm and hard work may encourage relatives and friends.

Above all, we hope that it will help them to realise that they are not alone, and that many are facing similar experiences.

Reggie, Brian and Silvia Dingwall

Preface to the Second Edition

It is now ten years since we wrote the first edition of this book. In that time there have been major changes in the National Health Service, not least in psychiatric services. The move towards community treatment that we remarked upon in 1987 has accelerated, and the important role of relatives in the care of people with severe mental illness is now formally recognised in a series of government initiatives. This means that the professionals' attitudes towards carers have improved considerably, but not that services for them have uniformly got better. There is still a long way to go.

It is in this context that we have revised our book, which describes and takes account of these new developments. When we reread the original, we were surprised at how dated it had become in a relatively short time. We hope that this new version will serve the same purpose as the old one, and continue to be of use.

Elizabeth Kuipers
Paul Bebbington
London, 1997

Authors' Acknowledgements

The revised edition of this book has benefited greatly from the constructive criticisms of Barbara Chaffey of the Mental Health Act Office at the Maudsley Hospital, London, and Kate Searle of Islington People's Rights. Our thanks are also due to the many relatives of psychiatric clients who have provided us with the necessary knowledge and incentive. Some have also commented on the book directly.

Introduction

This book is intended for the carers of people affected by mental illness. Everybody knows of someone who has had a 'nervous breakdown', and for large numbers of us this means someone in the family. But mental illness is even more widespread than most people realise, and not everyone is affected in the same way or to the same extent. In this book we have concentrated on the problems you may face if your relative (or friend) suffers from **schizophrenia** or **manic depressive illness**. These are among the most severe mental conditions, as well as being much more common than is generally recognised.

It is estimated, for instance, that more than a quarter of a million people in this country—the equivalent of the population of a medium-sized city such as Derby—suffer from either chronic or relapsing schizophrenia. To put it another way: two people every day suffer a first attack of schizophrenia. Manic depressive illness is even more common. Where we work in inner London, it is reckoned that about 15 per cent of the local people will be treated by a psychiatrist for depression at some time in their lives, although most of them will suffer relatively mild forms of the disorder. Psychiatrists do, of course, deal with other disorders, but these are mostly less severe; or, like dementia, they begin towards the end of a person's life.

Living with others always takes a certain amount of skill, and tensions inevitably arise from time to time. Not everyone is equally good at it, but most of us try hard to keep our relationships going reasonably satisfactorily. We learn to do this from a young age, by watching others and by building our own friendships—some short, some long-lasting.

If you live with someone who develops schizophrenia or manic depressive illness, you are almost certain to be presented with problems that you have never met before, and that you may never even have heard about from anyone else. Some people in this situation are lucky, and hit on good ways to cope with it from early on. Others don't cope so well, and this may lead to further and increasing difficulties. They then often blame themselves for the way things have turned out; but, while this is understandable, it is not appropriate. If there were courses available on how to live with someone suffering from a severe mental illness, it would perhaps be a different matter, but there aren't. In fact, although things are improving, there is still not much guidance to be had, so people try to adapt their previous experiences to deal with the new situation. Unfortunately, this new situation is so different from anything they have previously known that old and tried methods of coping may not work. It is because schizophrenia and manic depressive illness can lead to difficulties of a rather particular and persistent kind, both for sufferers and for their carers, that we have written this book specially for them.

These days the newspapers are full of stories about community care, mostly uncomplimentary. In fact, the policy of community care for people with mental illness is now nearly fifty years old. The driving force behind it was the idea that patients—clients, as we increasingly refer to them—should no longer be kept for long periods in the old and poorly maintained mental hospitals of the time. Instead, facilities were to be developed in the community—day hospitals, psychiatric wards in local general hospitals, day centres, group homes, hostels and the like. However, these new facilities have always lagged behind the closure of the services they were supposed to replace. The result, as you are likely to know, is that the burden of caring for the mentally ill has fallen increasingly upon their relatives.

Many psychiatrists and other health professionals are very concerned about the effects that community care has on the lives of clients and their carers. Overall, we think the policy is a good one in itself, with many potential benefits for clients. There is no doubt that in its early days it was very badly funded and implemented, and even now the service is seriously overstretched in many areas. This is particularly so in the inner cities. But the policy is clearly here to stay, and we all have to live with it, sufferers, carers and professionals together. In this less than ideal situation, we hope you will gain some support and help from this book.

In the past five years, the high level of public concern has encouraged a number of initiatives by the government to make community care work more effectively. While medication is important, the management of severe psychiatric illness has always required more than simple pill-pushing by doctors. People with severe mental illness need to be looked after ('monitored') in the way best suited to them, and in order to keep them well it may be necessary to help them make adjustments in the way they live. This may involve organising work and leisure activities and types of supported housing like hostels and group homes. It is also recognised that people do better if their care is the responsibility of a named person over a considerable period of time—the principle of 'continuity of care'.

In 1991 the Department of Health introduced the Care Programme Approach, which laid down guidelines for mental health teams in order to persuade them to work in the way described above. An important part of this approach is the involvement of clients and carers in decisions about care. These changes are so important that we have added a new chapter to deal with them (Chapter 3).

Another initiative is the Mental Health (Patients in the Community) Act of 1995, which in April 1996 brought in supervised discharge for some clients. This is an extension of the powers of the Mental Health Act of 1983 to take account of the fact that many more seriously ill people are now managed in their own homes rather than in hospital. This Act has consequences both for civil liberty and for effective management, and is discussed in full in Chapter 6.

If you live with someone who has schizophrenia or manic depressive illness, you must have many questions you would like answered. We have tried to think what these might be, and to answer them. The first chapter is mainly concerned with basic information about severe mental illness. We hope you won't find this too dry, but it has to cover a lot of ground. Chapter 2 deals with problems you may have to confront in living with your relative. Then, as already mentioned, Chapter 3 deals with community care. The next two chapters are devoted to the various types of services and treatments. The sixth chapter covers the legal processes surrounding compulsory admission and treatment, the safeguards that are built into the **1983 Mental Health Act**, and the very recent legislation introducing **Community Supervision Orders**. This section is important, but will only be relevant to a few of you who read this book. The last chapter considers the feelings you might have about your situation, and how you might cope with them. At the end are two appendices: the first, new to this edition, explains **how to find your way around the benefit system**; and the second is an updated and expanded **list of useful addresses**.

We hope that a quick glance will tell you whether the book will help you. You are bound to have questions we have not covered, so do not be afraid to ask the people treating and caring for your relative for answers and advice. It is essential that you realise the importance of the part that you can play in your relative's progress to recovery. Although you may sometimes feel discouraged, helping your relative can also be very rewarding—and it may be vital for him or her.

Mental illness is a field in which there are more uncertainties than facts. You may well come across professionals with very different views on particular subjects, and some will put them forward with total conviction! If you are not aware that mental health is an area where many questions are still waiting for an answer, this can be especially confusing. Sadly, although things have improved in the ten years since the first edition of this book, many professionals remain rather ignorant about the difficulties you are likely to experience in living with the mentally ill person. In fact, you are an expert in this field, in the sense that you have first-hand experience. And it may well be that you have already tried many of the suggestions that will be made to you here.

We have tried to avoid appearing to be certain when we aren't. After all, each situation is different. However, the suggestions we make have been found useful by other people in similar circumstances, and they may work for you.

Finally, we give examples from the situations and experiences of clients and relatives we have known. We think personal anecdotes add colour to, as well as substantiating, what we have to say, and you may be able to identify with some of the stories. In the interests of confidentiality, we have disguised the identities of the people we write about.

1 Mental Illness

Mental illness is a loose term. It covers problems that some people have in connection with the way they **think, feel** or **behave**. Medically speaking, it covers **several different conditions**, whose effects can range from a state of temporary distress to long-lasting incapacity.

It is sometimes difficult to distinguish mild states of, for instance, anxiety or depression, from ordinary experiences, and indeed the transition from what we think of as normal to the definitely abnormal is a gradual one. It is made more complicated because 'abnormal' can mean two different things: what is abnormal for a given person, and what would be abnormal for anyone. In general, we tend to think of mental states as abnormal when, as a result, the sufferer is clearly and persistently unable to function properly in society. This is important because once we recognise that an individual is psychiatrically abnormal, we are quite rightly prepared to make allowances for that person, at least to some extent, in a way we wouldn't if we thought he or she was merely misbehaving, or fooling about, or just being rather self-indulgent. This can be an issue even in the more severe psychiatric conditions that are the subject of this book.

For most of us mental illness is a disturbing and frightening thing. This is partly because people who are mentally ill can behave in **unpredictable, unfamiliar and sometimes embarrassing** ways. It is particularly distressing when these changes happen to someone who is close to us. Worst of all, the mentally ill make us feel **helpless**—the normal ways of helping people do not seem to work. It is hurtful and confusing when we try to be sympathetic and supportive, and offer constructive advice, to find it rejected or misinterpreted, or just plain ignored.

It is frequently said that mental illness is an illness like any other. This is not quite true, though: after all, we respond to illnesses of the mind in a rather special way. When someone is physically ill, there is no problem about understanding his or her behaviour, because we see the reason for it: we might behave the same way ourselves in similar circumstances. However, it may not be possible to uncover the reasons why mentally ill people behave as they do. Sometimes, the reasons are based on beliefs, held by the sufferers, that are obviously untrue or appear to us incredible; they may also claim to have experiences which seem quite fantastic. This is upsetting, and it is not surprising that people shy away from the topic of mental illness. They often use euphemisms like **suffering from nerves** or **nervous breakdown** to describe the sick person or his mental condition.

For these reasons, mental illness is still associated with many **myths** and **misunderstandings**. Those who have been mentally ill often feel, with some justification, that they are shunned and stigmatised by society. When we wrote the first edition, we felt that these attitudes were beginning to change. Now we are not so sure. Recent tragedies in which members of the public have been killed by people with severe mental disorders have been greeted by the most appalling headlines in tabloid newspapers. Clinicians and carers attempting to provide more information and encourage more open attitudes encounter an uphill battle in the face of such media exploitation. Some of this renewed stigma is probably a consequence of the community care policy, which inevitably means that people come across severe mental illness more often and are therefore obliged to form opinions about it based on direct experience, but with little guidance on what to expect or how to deal with it. It was perhaps easier to feel compassion for people who sometimes behave strangely when they lived in a large mental hospital fifteen miles away.

Although there is considerable evidence that the more severe forms may be caused by subtle changes in **brain chemistry**, psychiatrists cannot yet rely on any simple investigation, like a blood test, for finding out if someone has a particular mental illness. This being so, they can only recognise particular mental illnesses from the way people behave and the things they say. Doctors always feel that diagnosis, the business of recognising which illness someone has, is very important because, in theory at any rate, it narrows down the possibilities—the course the illness will take, the proper treatment to give, the likely response to it, and so on. Psychiatrists, too, are quite properly keen on diagnosis, even though it is particularly difficult in their chosen field. It is also less effective in its job of narrowing possibilities than in more precise branches of medicine. This makes psychiatry, with its many uncertainties, one of the most difficult specialties. In consequence, it is easy for misunderstandings to arise between clients, their relatives and the psychiatric team.

Experiencing a severe mental illness

Schizophrenia is one of the most severe mental illnesses. For a medical condition it is unusual in that it is seen all over the world with a very similar frequency, in both modern and traditional societies. It cannot, therefore, be said that it is one of the burdens of modern civilisation. It is now thought to be a little more common in males than in females, in whom it starts later and has a somewhat better outlook. It is more common among people lower down the social scale, but this seems likely to be the result of sufferers doing less well in life than they might otherwise have done.

Oddly, it might be best to start by saying what schizophrenia is **not**. It is **not**, despite what many people believe, a **split personality** of the Jekyll and Hyde type. There is no rapid switch from perfect normality to a totally different, often unpleasant, pattern of behaviour, so different that it is as if the individual has become someone else. This rather rare condition is called 'hysterical split personality', not schizophrenia.

The human mind has been described, fairly aptly, as being like an orchestra. The mind's separate functions—thought, sensation, memory, emotions and so on—can be perceived as the instruments that make up this orchestra. Normally these functions are integrated—that is, they play together in harmony. What seems to happen in schizophrenia is that this integration is somehow disrupted, or 'split'. It is as if the various instruments are all playing different tunes. The result in an orchestra would be an indescribable and painful jangling; the result for the mind is schizophrenia. And so it is not that the personality is split, but that the smooth dovetailing of the different functions of the mind is prevented. It is hard for those of us not affected to gain an insight into this terrible condition, but it results in sufferers being unable to trust their sensations and experiences and, by extension, the behaviour of those around them.

A doctor recognises schizophrenia mainly by the presence of **delusions**, **hallucinations** and **other unusual experiences**. Delusions are irrational beliefs, 'mad ideas', while hallucinations often take the form of imaginary voices. We describe these symptoms in more detail on pp. 24–6.

The problems may start suddenly and dramatically, but often follow a gradual deterioration: sufferers may become **less sociable** and **less able to study or work** in a consistent way. They may become **less affectionate**, so that relatives find it hard to get through to them any more. In cases like this, with a gradual onset, the definite features of schizophrenia may appear only after months or even years. This makes it difficult for the psychiatrist to be sure what is happening, at least at the beginning.

Mary was an eighteen-year-old who developed a schizophrenic illness. She still lived at home, and had always been a shy person. She was very close to her widowed father. She enjoyed quiet activities like fishing but would also go out to a pub or visit friends to play records. Over a period of some months, she felt less like going out. It made her feel very self-conscious, even a bit jittery. She did not really like the sense of being the centre of attention. However, she enjoyed the company of her friends, so she often invited them round. They were a bit boisterous and Mary was glad just to sit on the sidelines watching them. It made her feel safe. However, because they were noisy, the neighbours complained one night, with the result that her father discouraged her from asking them round again, so she didn't.

She began to find that her usual daily tasks were a real effort and, eventually, beyond her. When her elder brother came round one evening he dragged her out to a local pub, but Mary did not want to go and felt dreadful when she got there. She felt as if everyone was looking at her, that somehow they knew all about her and were talking about her. She made an excuse to leave as early as possible, but was still upset when she got home. The next evening something happened that made her feel even more frightened. While she was in her bedroom, she could hear people talking about her. There seemed no doubt about it, although when she looked out of the window and the door there was no one around. Moreover, the voices, whoever they were, were not being very nice about her, using language and making suggestions that upset her. She kept very quiet about this for a couple of days. However, she began to have strange fancies that seemed to grip her imagination—for instance, that she was pregnant. She thought she could feel the baby stirring inside her. As she had never made love with anyone, she thought that she could only have been made pregnant by a spirit or a ghost, and the more she thought about this the more convinced she became.

Finally, Mary told her father what had been going on, and he called the family doctor immediately.

This story gives some idea of what it was like for one person who developed schizophrenia. The experience differs in detail from case to case, but it is rarely anything but very unpleasant. The experiences Mary had, and some that she didn't, will be described further when we write about the symptoms of the illness. It is important to remember that what is a symptom to the doctor or relative is a very real and often very terrifying experience to the sufferer.

Fortunately, Mary responded well to treatment and got completely better, although she remained a rather shy and immature young woman. Clearly, it would have been very difficult for anyone to be sure what was going on in the early stages of this illness, or that it was anything more than 'just a phase'. Once the full picture emerged, however, there could be no doubt that Mary had schizophrenia.

There are, in fact, two sorts of symptoms in schizophrenia. Hallucinations and delusions may be rather dramatic, but they aren't usually present all the time. It is the **negative symptoms**, described on p. 28, that are really damaging. If the individual doesn't have any negative symptoms, he or she may be fairly well between attacks of the more dramatic kind. And some lucky people may have only a single attack.

Simon was like this. He was a thirty-three-year-old married man who worked as an electrical engineer. He seemed to have been a cheerful and effective member of society before his illness. Following what appeared to be a minor problem at work, he suddenly became very frightened, and claimed that the local radio mast was controlling his brain. He was admitted to hospital, where he was observed for a few days without being given any medication. His state of mind rapidly improved, and after a few weeks he was able to take up his ordinary life again. So far he has not had any return of his mental symptoms.

What we call schizophrenia may in fact be a number of different illnesses, so it is hardly surprising that doctors sometimes find it difficult to give exact guidance about outlook, the need for particular treatments and so on. The problems most commonly begin in early adulthood: two-thirds of sufferers will have had their first attack by the time they are thirty. However, it can develop at any time of life, right up into old age.

Maude was a seventy-one-year-old woman who had followed a career in the civil service with some success. She was widowed and her children lived in the next town. Some time before, she had had a minor difference of opinion with her next-door neighbour, and she became rather embarrassed whenever she met him as the problem had never really been resolved. This got worse, so that she would avoid his eye rather than say good morning. Not surprisingly, the neighbour was not sure how to respond to this snub and was rather embarrassed himself. Maude took this as indicating that he was ashamed of something, although she wasn't sure what. However, this gradually became clear to her: his shifty behaviour must be the result of something he was up to, and Maude reckoned that other little pieces of evidence confirmed that he was secretly making bombs for a terrorist group. This explained the rather unusual chemical smell she thought she could detect lingering about her own house and garden. Her children were never able to pick up this smell and were surprised at her allegations about the neighbour, whom they had always previously found rather pleasant. Nor were they convinced by her claim that his wife had been passing messages to fellow conspirators by the order in which she hung clothes on the garden line.

Schizophrenia is very rare indeed before adolescence. It seems to require that the brain has matured to a certain point before it will emerge. Sometimes it comes out of the blue. Some sufferers, on the other hand, have always had eccentric, quirky or withdrawn personalities; but it must be said that most people like that do not develop schizophrenia.

Manic depressive illness is the other great mental affliction of adult life. About twice as many women as men suffer from it, and it, too, is widespread throughout the world. Many authorities think it may be on the increase, but the most severe types are probably becoming less common. Once more, it is probably not one but several conditions, and this is reflected in the many overlapping names that psychiatrists use. However, these conditions are grouped together because their central feature is a disorder of mood. By 'mood' is meant feelings like happiness, sadness, fear or anger.

The word 'depression' is often used in a casual way to describe anything from normal unhappiness to those abnormal moods that seem to be the result of an illness—and it is true that it may sometimes be hard to draw the line between the two. The mood disturbance in manic depressive illness centres on happiness or sadness. However, this disturbance is far greater and more persistent than most of us normally experience. Sufferers are either hopelessly gloomy and miserable, looking at things in a very pessimistic light (**depression**) or wildly elated and energetic with big ideas about themselves and their abilities (**mania**). Manic depressive illness is sometimes called **affective illness** (from the word 'affect' in the sense of 'mood').

One big division that can be drawn is between those who get both depressed and manic, and those who only get depressed. The first group are called **bipolar** because they move between the two **poles** of depression and elation, and the second group are described as **unipolar**. So you may hear clinicians referring to unipolar or bipolar affective illness. The bipolar type often begins in early adult life, whereas unipolar illness is more likely to emerge as people get older. Bipolar illness is actually quite rare—indeed, rarer than schizophrenia—and most sufferers oscillate between normal mood and depression. Unlike unipolar affective disorder, which is commoner in women, bipolar disorder affects the sexes equally.

Another distinction you may hear about is that between depressive neurosis (or neurotic depression) and depressive psychosis (or psychotic depression). Psychosis and neurosis are terms that have lost their original meaning and have failed to acquire any very exact new meaning. Perhaps precisely because they can be used so vaguely, they have remained rather popular with psychiatrists. In general, a depressive psychosis is a severe depression, often with odd symptoms, and sometimes with very odd ones like hallucinations and delusions (see pp. 24–6). A depressive neurosis looks more like an extreme form of normal misery, perhaps persisting because the sufferer has a rather vulnerable personality. However, the two categories run into one another without much evidence of a clear boundary—there are many people whose condition falls midway between the two types.

However much clinicians may argue the finer points (and they do), a depressive illness makes a harrowing experience.

Susan was a twenty-four-year-old teacher who had married about three years previously. She and her husband had moved to London, where they had bought a pleasant modern flat. She worked in a local infant school. She liked the work, although she did have opinions about teaching that had led to minor disagreements with the headmistress. Working as an infant teacher is always strenuous, but Susan usually had energy to spare.

However, over a period of a few weeks, she was feeling as though the work was becoming too much for her. She felt really tired when she got home, and unable to devote herself to the preparations she normally made for the next day's teaching. She usually cooked the evening meal—something she did efficiently and almost automatically—but this, too, she found had become a real effort. She somehow got through her days, but then lay around in the evening in an exhausted state. In the past, she and her husband had enjoyed going out together, but she now felt this to be completely beyond her: she made excuses and her husband fell in with this quieter life fairly amicably, feeling merely that she was going through a tough patch at school and would benefit from the rest. He was solicitous and tried to support and comfort her.

One evening, although he had a suspicion that this might be difficult, he moved from gentle affection into love-making. This distressed Susan a lot although she tried, not very successfully, to hide it. Not being able to respond sexually was bad enough, but she also felt completely out of touch with her normal affection for him, almost as if he were a stranger. She began to feel that a woman like this couldn't be much good, and her sense of guilt grew laceratingly painful. She became unable to think of anything except her agonising preoccupation with herself and her feelings. She could hardly do anything and she felt slow, stupid and old. Her husband, meanwhile, was becoming increasingly and desperately worried about her. She still forced herself to go to work, but one morning the burden became too much and she walked out of school and went home without telling anyone. She phoned her husband, who came home and called their family doctor.

Although at first it sounds quite similar, John's story is rather different. A little older than Susan, he too became depressed over a period of weeks. He stayed at home and was visited by his family doctor, who gave him antidepressant tablets. He seemed to be responding to this treatment and his doctor was pleased with his progress.

John now felt pretty good and quite enthusiastic about going back to his work as a telephone engineer. He rang up his personnel officer to arrange it, and told his wife that, as he was completely recovered, there was not much point in staying at home. When he got to work on his first day back, he found that a number of relatively easy tasks had been set aside for him. He completed these very quickly and without difficulty, and felt very pleased with the way things had gone. He was pleased, too, to see his workmates, and rapidly overcame their slight awkwardness at having him back after 'a bit of mental trouble'. In fact, as he was feeling quite jokey, he soon had them all laughing and relaxed. His manager was also glad to have him back so obviously recovered.

Over the next two days John became convinced that one particular working practice, which previously he had put up with as a bit of a chore, was in fact grossly inefficient. He thought out how things actually should be done, and was certain that it would be a major change for the better if this new routine was brought in. He accordingly asked to see the manager, who was somewhat taken aback when he found out why John had requested the interview. He raised a number of fairly obvious objections to John's proposal, although he acknowledged that it had some good points. John expounded his view fairly forcefully, and left feeling that the manager was more stupid than he had thought. He did not, however, let this blight his day. When he returned from work, he told his wife all about it.

That evening he had an idea. His car was almost due for a service: he would save himself money by doing it himself. He drove off and bought a large can of oil, then returned to his garage where he carried out an oil change. Although he knew in principle how to do this, he had never done it before and made rather a mess. However, this was a minor consideration compared with the sense of satisfaction with which he returned, rather dirty, to the house. His wife looked unsure when he said he proposed to service the car regularly, but he felt she was being unadventurous and a bit of a killjoy. She confirmed his opinion by going to bed at eleven o'clock. John didn't fancy sleeping just yet so he played some Mozart, music he had always been fond of. Tonight it seemed particularly pleasing.

It was around four a.m. that the great idea struck him—no less than a completely new way of transmitting telephone messages. It was like a blinding light in its brilliant simplicity. He rummaged out a large and out-of-date diary and began to put his ideas on paper—he was terrified they would leave him before he could get them down. His wife found him still scribbling when she came down in the morning. He said he wasn't going to work as he had something important to work on at home. However, at ten a.m. he went out, and when he came back he told his wife that he had drawn some money out of the bank to finance a business venture designed to develop and market his new telephone system. The enthusiastic and naïve way in which he talked about this led her to call the family doctor. John was not pleased to see her, as he was feeling very good indeed.

John's experiences would be regarded as typical of a bipolar manic depressive illness.

There can be no doubt from the descriptions above that depression is a very unpleasant experience indeed. So too, sometimes, is mania, because the sufferer may feel very irritable and 'pressured'. However, John actually felt good with his illness—and this can pose real problems, particularly if sufferers, while denying that they are ill, do things that they will later greatly regret. Getting such people to cooperate in treatment can be very difficult indeed.

Manic depressive disorders typically come on in separate **attacks**, and the client is usually fairly well in between. In either type, attacks may develop over a few days, but sufferers from the unipolar condition often become depressed gradually over a period of weeks or months.

Compared with physical illness, mental disorders do last quite a long time. Psychiatrists are used to this, but you may not be. However, things have improved. Before effective treatment was available, attacks might last from six months to two years, but nowadays six months is usually the maximum, and many episodes are considerably shorter. Attacks of bipolar illness tend to be shorter than with the unipolar version, but may occur more frequently.

Many sufferers have only one attack of depression, but the majority do relapse. This often happens after years of good health. Once a pattern of relapse has developed, the gaps between attacks may tend to shorten, although this is not always the case. Some people may be persistently depressed, and this can cause great problems—as you will know if you live with such a person.

Negative symptoms (see p. 28) do occur in manic depressive illness, but much less commonly than in schizophrenia. Occasionally it may be difficult for the psychiatrist to decide whether someone is suffering from schizophrenia or from manic depressive illness. This is less worrying than it sounds, for in borderline cases treatment is determined by the features of the illness rather than by its particular label. Sometimes these intermediate illnesses are called **schizoaffective disorder**. They are treated rather like schizophrenia but behave more like manic depressive illness.

Causes

Severe mental illness seems to have no simple cause. It is often suggested that several factors work together to produce it. However, there are people who are subject to all these factors but who never become mentally ill. Equally, there are people with mental illness who seem to have none of the risk factors. Our knowledge of the origins of mental illness is a long way from being **complete**, despite years of effort and research.

Some mental illnesses **run in families**. This is true of both schizophrenia and manic depressive illness, to a roughly similar degree. The best evidence for this comes from the study of twins. Of the two sorts of twins, those that come from a single fertilised egg and those that come from two separate eggs, the first are genetically identical—that is, they share all the genetic instructions that determine their characteristics. The second type are really just like ordinary brothers and sisters, but who happen to have been born at the same time; although they are closely related, on average they share only half their genetic instructions, so they are non-identical. If these mental illnesses are genetically determined, you would expect the identical twin of someone with schizophrenia to have a much greater chance of developing the disorder than the non-identical twin of such a person. When groups of identical and of non-identical twins are compared, this is what is actually found. And it means that the tendency to such illnesses is 'built in', at least partly.

This tendency, whether in relation to twins of either sort or to other relatives, may worry sufferers, and indeed may have worried you: where one person is affected there is indeed a risk, usually small, that other members of the family will also develop the illness. This is an important topic, so we discuss it at some length on pp. 59–60.

Schizophrenia may sometimes also result from significant damage to the brain—what the medical profession in a nice piece of understatement calls a 'physical insult'.

Complications and difficulties during pregnancy and at birth are more common in babies who as adults develop schizophrenia. This probably means that in some cases **damage in the very early stages of life** may itself result in a tendency to the condition, although it does not appear until much later. We have no idea how this delayed reaction actually works. In rare instances, schizophrenia can even follow a **physical cause in adult life**—a head injury, epilepsy, or certain uncommon bodily diseases. In most cases the connection is pretty clear because the physical condition produces its own symptoms by which it is readily recognised. Recognisable physical causes for manic depressive illness are also rare, but do occur—for instance, in association with abnormalities of the endocrine glands.

More recently, some workers have claimed to have discovered evidence that schizophrenia can be caused by a virus. The evidence is not conclusive, and it is unlikely to account for many cases. But in the 1920s and 1930s the viral epidemic of encephalitis lethargica did indeed result in many cases of schizophrenia. Of the other infections associated with the features both of schizophrenia and of manic depressive illness the most famous was syphilis of the brain, otherwise known as general paresis of the insane (GPI). Although this played havoc among the Victorians, eminent and otherwise, it is now so rare that we have seen only a handful of cases in our professional lives. It is almost unimaginable that your relative's illness is due to GPI, although the relevant blood tests are still carried out as routine. Syphilis itself is now a rare disease, and early treatment with antibiotics has effectively eliminated the slow progression to brain infection that used to follow it.

The evidence that both schizophrenia and manic depressive illness are associated with changes in various **transmitter substances** in the brain is now strong. The nerve cells in the brain, which form a sort of network, work by switching each other on and off—a bit like the switches in a computer. One cell helps to switch on the next in line by giving out a chemical, or transmitter substance. The brain uses several of these substances in different places, and it is believed that if they are not being released in the right quantities and the right places mental illness can result. We are even in a position to make reasonable guesses about which transmitters, and in which parts of the brain they are located. Quite a lot of evidence, for instance, suggests that in schizophrenia there is some abnormality in the handling of the transmitter substance **dopamine**, particularly in the connections between the deeper parts of the brain and the areas nearer the surface (the cerebral cortex) where the more intellectual functions of the mind, such as perception, thought and judgement, are carried out. In crude terms, it is as if there is too much dopamine around. Every drug that improves the clinical condition of someone with acute symptoms of schizophrenia also suppresses the action of dopamine.

Nowadays it is generally argued that the dopamine theory does not account for all the features of schizophrenia. For instance, it is difficult to explain why schizophrenia typically does not arise in childhood or early adolescence. More elaborate theories now suggest that the dopamine abnormality arises as the long-term effect of an earlier disturbance in nerve cells that use glutamate as a transmitter substance. These are located in a part of the underside of the brain called the hippocampus, and may be damaged or caused to malfunction either before the individual was born or in early childhood.

Another biological influence on these several mental illnesses is that exerted by the body's hormonal state. Some authorities have tried to explain the greater frequency of depression in women in terms of the action of the sex hormones. It used to be thought that the menopause was associated with an increase in depressive illnesses in women. It is possible that this hormonal change may occasionally have an effect, but it cannot account for many cases. Much more significant are the hormonal changes brought about by childbirth. These can lead to the so-called **post-**

partum ('after-delivery') **psychoses**, which can take the form of schizophrenia or, more often, of manic depressive illness, and often show features of both. This condition is relatively rare, occurring after only one pregnancy in five hundred. Sufferers rarely show negative symptoms (see p. 28), and there is a very good projected outcome for the attack itself. Further attacks occur after about one in five subsequent deliveries, and about half the sufferers have later attacks that do not follow delivery. Hormones may also play a part in **post-natal depression**, a much milder, though still unpleasant, condition. But there are almost certainly social and psychological influences at work here as well. The Association for Post-Natal Illness can offer advice (see Appendix 2).

The best evidence for the hormonal explanation of depressive disorder concerns the stress hormone cortisol. The control of this hormone and its effects does not seem to be associated with gender, so the hormonal theory cannot explain why women are more prone to depression.

Personality, which is a mixture of the temperament you are born with and the effects of subsequent experiences, may play some part in increasing the risk of developing a mental illness. Attempts have been made to link schizophrenia with a particular personality type—the 'schizoid personality'. Such people are aloof, sensitive, solitary and not good at making emotional contact. However, there are many people like this who never develop schizophrenia. People who **behave** increasingly like this may indeed be showing the first signs of schizophrenia, but that is a rather different matter.

A number of personality types have been implicated in manic depressive illnesses. One is the 'cyclothymic' personality—people like this are moody, in the sense that sometimes they are energetic and enthusiastic and sometimes gloomy and lethargic. It is possible that this personality type manifests minor degrees of the mood swings that, if fully developed, would be called bipolar illness, so it is not surprising that people who seem to fall into this category sometimes make the move into a fully fledged illness. However, it is sometimes those who are persistently energetic and cheerful who surprise us by having a 'nervous breakdown'—and we often describe such an individual as 'the last person you would have expected to have one'. This is the hypomanic personality, and people like this do indeed sometimes develop a severe depressive illness. Because those around them may be slow to recognise it, they may occasionally kill themselves before anyone realises the danger.

Another type of personality that often has a tendency to develop depressive illnesses is actually called the 'depressive personality'. Here we probably see the result of innate temperament, but people with this personality are most noticeable on account of their rather gloomy attitudes, which they are likely to have learned from their experience of life. They have a distorted view of themselves and the world, such that any new experience is interpreted in a gloomy and hopeless way. For such people nothing good can ever happen because, if it did, they wouldn't notice it or would find some way of devaluing it.

Finally, some people who are prone to depression are very obsessive and perfectionist. Because nothing is good enough for them, they can never feel good about things they have done. For most of us, 'Nobody's perfect' is a solace; for them it is a reproach.

In all probability, little can be done about basic temperament. However, using the techniques of **cognitive therapy** (see p. 120), therapists have recently made successful attempts to change the attitudes of individuals with a persistent depressive outlook.

Both schizophrenia and manic depressive illness are also influenced by the **stresses and strains of everyday living**. Such stresses can take the form of some sudden misfortune or change in living circumstances, or more enduring difficulties. Problems that most people manage to cope with seem to be able to push a few into mental illness, probably because of an existing tendency that way. But such illness also sometimes occurs without being preceded by any obvious stress, and this makes the experience even more incomprehensible and upsetting for sufferer, friends and relatives alike.

At one time there was a theory that schizophrenia was the result of an abnormal family environment in childhood. The best-known proponent of this idea in Britain was the late R. D. Laing. The research on this was never very good, and is now discounted. It did frequently have the unproductive effect of making the unhappy parents of those who later developed schizophrenia feel both guilty and defensive. It has also had a pervasive and unfortunate influence on the attitudes of some mental health professionals towards the parents of people with schizophrenia, which lingers even today.

There is rather better evidence, though, that unfortunate circumstances and experiences in childhood can make people prone to develop depression when they are grown up.

It is well established that sufferers from schizophrenia are affected by tensions at home, but this is not very surprising, and it is hardly the same thing as claiming that the behaviour of parents can *cause* schizophrenia. A similar relationship between domestic tensions and manic depressive illness has now been found, and this does carry the hope that, once they know how they might do it, relatives may be able to change things for the benefit of the sufferer. This is discussed further on pp. 121–2.

There has also been considerable research into the possibility that **diet**, **infections** or **allergic processes** may lie behind the development of severe mental illness. This research has not been very productive, and it must be concluded that if these factors do have any affect it is only in rare cases or to a minor extent.

This summary of our knowledge about the causes of these severe mental illnesses may lead you to think that the enormous effort put into research has not reaped much in the way of reward. This is not entirely true. We think that the slow progress is due to the fact that these conditions are actually extremely complex and subtle. Indeed, if they were not, if they didn't arise from very subtle imbalances in brain function, they probably would not show themselves so clearly and purely as mental illnesses. Because of this it seems rather unlikely that there will be any sudden breakthrough: research will find the answers gradually by piecing together what is almost certainly a very complicated jigsaw.

Symptoms

We are now going to take you through the symptoms of schizophrenia and manic depressive illness.

Many of these you may immediately recognise from your own relative's behaviour. Others you will not be familiar with, but we think it is useful both to learn as much as possible about what can happen to people's behaviour as a result of illness and to avoid being caught unawares by new developments. We will concentrate particularly on those symptoms that are distressing, confusing or frequent.

Mental illness frequently shows itself through **changes in mood**, even when this is not the central feature of the disorder. Normally most of us keep on a fairly even keel, although sometimes we may feel especially happy or a bit fed up. The mood of people with mental illness is much more extreme than most of us ever experience. This comes across in the story of Susan, above.

People can be said to be depressed in mood when they remain sad, miserable, mournful or gloomy for days or weeks at a time, and when this mood **persists** despite all the efforts of themselves and those around them. One of the most characteristic symptoms is that the sufferer can no longer take pleasure in anything at all. Depressed people feel pessimistic and hopeless about themselves and the world, frequently **blaming themselves** for everything that goes wrong. They withdraw into themselves and don't talk much. Their energy goes, they are easily tired and they let things slide. In general, they cannot be bothered any more, and they often lose interest in sex. They may feel that they are so worthless that there is nothing left but to end things as quickly as possible—by an overdose, or in a more violent manner. Those who do intend **suicide** will usually give some warning (see pp. 45–6).

In some people the loss of energy is very marked indeed. They move more slowly than they normally do, and often complain that they are walking as though they were twenty or thirty years older than they actually are. Sometimes, they may stop moving much at all, staying in bed most of the time. Occasionally an individual will develop an extreme condition called 'depressive stupor'. In this state he or she does not talk or move, and may even become completely incontinent. This is very rare now, but was not uncommon in the days before effective treatment prevented things going so far.

Some depressed people become very **agitated**. They cannot keep still and often pace from room to room wringing their hands. They may continually ask their relatives and friends for reassurance—'I'm not going mad, am I?' 'It will be all right, won't it?' This distress is painful to see and, if you have seen it, you will know that at the same time it can be extremely wearing.

Disturbed sleep is common in the mentally ill. Some people have trouble getting off to sleep, often because of depressing or worrying thoughts. Others sleep fitfully and restlessly. Some depressed people wake up in the very early morning, a time when they often feel at their worst. They lie there in anguish, feeling crushed beneath the weight of their sorrows. Those with mania can frequently manage with very little sleep, remaining energetic into the small hours, then waking early and refreshed. People who have been mentally ill for some time occasionally develop odd ways of living, waking at night and sleeping by day. This is usually part of a general tendency to avoid people.

Because depression makes people feel **physically run down**, with ordinary aches and pains becoming more noticeable, they sometimes do not realise they are depressed, but think they must have some physical disease. This may come out as a fear of cancer or AIDS or venereal disease, and occasionally leads to a preoccupation with physical health that can be very tiresome for relatives. Because the sufferer may emphasise bodily aspects, the family doctor may not at first recognise the depression underlying the complaints, and may embark on unwarranted investigations and treatment. This mistake is easily made, and not uncommon.

Margaret was a woman in late middle age who began to feel run down. At first she attributed this to the fact that she was not as young as she used to be. She had always been a fastidious person of orderly habits, and she took more notice than other people might of an increasing tendency in herself to be constipated. What she didn't realise was that constipation is not infrequent in depression—part of the general slowing that happens in moderately severe cases. She became very preoccupied with her bowels, so much so that she could not be bothered to go out socially any more. She began to notice pains in her stomach. She visited her family doctor who prescribed a laxative, but without much effect. Her appetite declined. At this point, she read a newspaper story about a television star who had died of cancer. She didn't tell anyone about this, but gradually came to the fearful conclusion that her own symptoms were probably the result of cancer of the bowel. She was overwhelmed with anxiety, which she bottled up for some time until at last she brought herself to return to her doctor. He took her seriously and referred her for investigations. This time he spotted that she was depressed, but thought it was a natural reaction to her fear of cancer. When the investigations proved negative, the gastroenterologist deduced that she was greatly exaggerating her symptoms and referred her to a psychiatrist colleague. Fortunately, she was able to identify the true nature of Margaret's problem.

In contrast, some mentally ill people become 'high': what the psychiatrist calls **hypomanic** or **manic**. This is what happened to John (p. 13). Such individuals are full of energy and ideas, and talk quickly and wittily. They race about getting things done (some of which are useful, some not). They may be found cleaning the cooker at four a.m., or may wake up the family at a similar time for an unplanned trip to the country. There is a danger that they may seriously exhaust themselves and, indeed, in the days before we had adequate sedation, it was not that rare for mania to cause death from exhaustion. Sufferers may get very **irritable** with those around them who try to impose a limit on their activity and on their wild schemes. They are often what the psychiatrist calls **disinhibited**—if they feel like doing or saying something, they will go ahead without regard for the consequences. This may be very hurtful. They frequently make new relationships with people they would not normally get on with. A few clients swing wildly from depression to elation in a manner that is very difficult to cope with indeed.

Some people may **lose their emotional responses** through mental illness, becoming wooden and unreactive, however hard you try to get through to them. This can happen with depressive illness—a person can become so frozen in his or her depressed mood as to seem untouched by anything. However, this is much more common and persistent in chronic schizophrenia, where it may be the central feature of the condition. People's faces usually show a constantly changing pattern of emotions and expressions, something so normal we don't even think about it until we are surprised by its absence. But in some cases of schizophrenia the facial expression is relatively fixed. This is unsettling. We feel unable to reach the person any more, and he or she seems very unrewarding to be with, so much do we rely on facial expression for the feeling of being in contact with the other person.

Normally, it is possible to have an effect on someone else's mood. In particular, we can usually cheer up friends and relatives who are feeling down. One of the upsetting things about the change in mood which occurs in mental illness is that it does not seem to respond to our efforts, and certainly not to those of the ill person.

Another of the symptoms of severe mental illness is a belief in things that are wildly improbable, or impossible. Other people's arguments or evidence fail to shift such ideas. Rigid and irrational beliefs of this sort are called **delusions**, and sufferers who act on them may get into a lot of difficulty and trouble with those around them. Some believe they are being **persecuted**, perhaps even by members of their own family. This may lead to arguments, and even fights. One man thought the IRA were leaving cars parked in particular places as a signal to him that they were on to him. Others, especially those who are manic, may have **unrealistically big ideas** about themselves and their abilities. This may lead them to spend money wildly or to develop grand schemes—they may even be able to persuade others to take part in them. One individual obtained a £10,000 loan from his ordinarily hard-headed bank manager to finance a completely cock-eyed business scheme.

Depressed people may be preoccupied with some imaginary wrong they have done, and feel horribly **guilty**. One elderly woman thought that she might have allowed a cannabis plant to grow in her garden and that the police were coming to take her away for trial and inevitable execution. Others may develop the idea that they are riddled with **cancer** or **venereal disease**.

People who have had delusions for some time may become wise to the fact that others quite obviously do not share them. They may then keep quiet about their ideas, which reduces further any likelihood that they may be swayed by the contrary views of others. Their delusions may still make their behaviour unpredictable and hard to fathom, even if they don't talk about their beliefs. Some advice on coping with delusions is given on pp. 38–40.

Many people with schizophrenia and some with manic depression imagine they hear things, often voices talking. This is an example of the sort of splitting we were describing earlier: thoughts and ideas are split off, so that they no longer appear as internal private experiences but are projected on to the outside world. Sometimes these voices may say things that upset the sufferer, who may then act in a strange or violent way. He or she may shout back at them, go round to sort out neighbours in the belief that they are making personal comments, or make complaints at the local police station. Hearing voices in this way is usually a most unpleasant experience, although sometimes people get used to them and for a few they provide comfort and company. Although, clearly, not something the rest of us can hear, these voices are real experiences for the sufferer. Even if they are distorted, or disguised as 'the devil' or as 'my neighbour', they often discuss areas of genuine concern to the person who hears them. It used to be thought that hearing voices was itself a sign of a severe mental illness, but it is now known that such experiences are not uncommon. A surprisingly large proportion of the general population have sometimes heard disembodied voices, but in most cases the experience is fleeting and has very little impact. We now think that it is the meaning, the distress and the problems that such experiences *cause* that are most crucial in diagnosing the sufferer's condition. The psychiatric term for such voices is **auditory hallucinations**.

Hallucinations may also be of things seen, although this is more unusual. One man had visions of choirs of angels when he became manic, but when he was depressed he saw the most dreadful and excruciating torments of hell. Other sufferers, particularly those with schizophrenia, may smell or taste things that aren't there. People experiencing such hallucinations may accuse relatives, neighbours or friends of trying to gas or poison them. One woman was convinced that the man in the flat above had built a pipe into her wall and was passing nerve gas into her sitting-room.

People may sometimes have hallucinations of touch. One unfortunate woman with schizophrenia felt hands going around her neck to strangle her as she walked down the street. Sometimes she would have some insight into this and be able to tell herself that the experience was unreal. At other times the power of the hallucination completely convinced her of its reality. This was very terrifying indeed, as you might imagine; she felt she was about to die and there was nothing she or anyone else could do about it. Other hallucinations may have a sexual aspect: people with schizophrenia may occasionally claim they have a phantom lover because of strange and unprovoked sexual sensations.

People with schizophrenia sometimes have other **odd experiences**. They may encounter odd changes in their own thinking. They may feel that somehow their thoughts can flow out beyond the boundaries of their own heads so that other people can pick them up and know what they are thinking. Then the mental flow may suddenly stop, leaving them puzzled by the odd sensation of a mind completely empty. This can lead them to accuse people of taking away their thoughts—of 'scraping her brain', as one woman put it. Sufferers may also feel that some of the thoughts in their heads don't belong to them, that they are completely alien, that they have been inserted or dropped into their heads from outside, like a stone into a pool. Others may feel that other people can interfere with or control what they are thinking or doing. One man thought the BBC had half of his brain on a computer and could program his thoughts and actions.

These experiences are so strange that it is quite hard for us to have any insight into what it must be like to have them. This again separates the sufferer with schizophrenia from the rest of us.

Schizophrenia and mania can both affect the ability to think straight in a sometimes spectacular way. The connection between thoughts becomes much less obvious, the sufferer's mind jumping from topic to topic in an unpredictable way. This usually reveals itself in disjointed speech. In mania it may still be possible to detect the connections, although they might be ones we would never think of ourselves. But sometimes in schizophrenia there appears to be no connection at all between sentences, and in extreme cases the link between words in the same sentence may also vanish. This makes the sufferer's speech incomprehensible, as may be imagined. Disordered speech is most common in acute episodes of illness, but may also be seen in chronic schizophrenia.

One thing you may worry about particularly in connection with a mentally ill relative is the question of violent behaviour. People with a severe mental illness are, as a group, somewhat more prone to violence than the rest of the population. This certainly does not apply to all, especially as mental illness often makes people **withdraw** from friends and relatives and become **apathetic**. But when an individual does behave violently while he or she is ill, such violence is disturbing, as it is often unforeseen. There are three broad types of violence, any or all of which may be shown by the same person.

The first arises from the increased **irritability** of some mentally ill people—they are on a shorter fuse than normal. The violence is understandable, but it is nonetheless an excessive reaction to the situation. Such violence can be avoided if relatives and friends are aware that it may occur, notice when it is about to, and immediately change tack. It is likely to happen when you have to refuse something your relative asks for, or disagree with what he or she says.

The second type of violence involves the individual striking out unexpectedly at someone near by. Afterwards, it is possible to see that the violent reaction was indeed provoked by the other person's action, but only because it was misinterpreted. It could not have been anticipated that the other's behaviour would be so provocative. One man with schizophrenia, Alan, had become preoccupied with the belief that his body was changing sex. A friend commented in a friendly way that he seemed to have put on a bit of weight recently, and was surprised when Alan struck him. Alan had taken the comment as a confirmation of his worst fears.

The third type is much rarer. It is planned by the sufferer, but arises because of **delusional beliefs** about his or her circumstances, and so is extremely difficult to predict. Sometimes the person gives warning—obviously, such warnings should be taken very seriously.

One man with schizophrenia had delusions of persecution, feeling that people were out to harm him. He kept these ideas to himself, so that his family was astonished when he made a murderous attack on a favourite uncle. It later turned out that he suspected his uncle of orchestrating the whole campaign against him.

Violent and murderous behaviour by people with schizophrenia has received a lot of publicity recently. The best-known example in Britain is perhaps Christopher Clunis, who murdered Jonathan Zito at a tube station in London. While this was an appalling tragedy for the victim and his family, and indeed for the perpetrator as well, it should be emphasised that such murders have **not** become more common, occurring in Britain over the last twenty-five years at a consistent annual rate of around twenty. And this is during a period when the general homicide rate has gradually risen, so the proportion of murders committed by people with mental disorder has actually fallen.

Depressed people occasionally take sudden and unexpected violent actions. What usually happens is that their depression is so deep that they see no future for themselves or their immediate family. Such people may kill relatives from a misplaced sense of pity. The newspapers occasionally carry stories of a mother or father who has murdered their children and then killed themselves. However, such tragedies are fortunately very rare. They serve to illustrate that violence is sometimes a possibility when judgement is impaired by mental illness. Violence is always difficult to cope with, but we have provided some guidelines on pp. 52–6, in the hope that they will help those of you who are faced with it.

The so-called **negative symptoms** are some of the most difficult that relatives have to come to terms with. Some sufferers, usually those who have been ill for some time, 'lose' bits of their normal behaviour. They cannot concentrate for long, they lose interest, they have no 'get-up-and-go'. They may sit around listlessly, watching television though taking in very little. They may lie in bed for long periods and avoid people. They may stop looking after themselves, becoming very untidy and rather careless about personal hygiene. Table manners deteriorate and other social graces may vanish. They lose the ability to react emotionally, seeming careless of people they used to be close to. They may even seem to be less intelligent than before. At the same time they become stubborn. All in all, these so-called negative symptoms, almost invariably the consequences of prolonged schizophrenia, are amongst the most difficult burdens that relatives have to bear. This is partly because it is quite hard to see them as resulting from illness, rather than from laziness, lack of feeling or even sheer bloody-mindedness.

Most mentally ill people are quite aware that something is wrong with the way they think and feel. However, in the more severe illnesses, **insight can be lost**. The sufferer cannot see that his or her beliefs are irrational and may express the oddest ideas with considerable vehemence. If your relative is like this, you may sometimes have found yourself being steered into arguing with him or her—although you probably realised that it was quite pointless. However, when the belief is merely improbable—for instance, one Cypriot housewife in London believed she was being persecuted by the Palestine Liberation Front—relatives may occasionally find themselves wondering if there might not be some truth in what the sufferer is saying. Sometimes, if they are easily swayed, they may even act as if they too believe what he or she claims. One rather shy young man developed a severe depressive illness in which he believed that he had raped a girl he had talked to on a couple of occasions about ten years previously. He thought the police were going to come for him and kill him. He managed to persuade his mother, with whom he lived, that this might be true. The desk sergeant at the local police station was surprised to receive a call from her, asking to speak to 'George the exterminator'. We will discuss how to cope with delusional ideas on pp. 38–40.

Outlook

Is there a cure for mental illness? There may be no clear answer to this question. There is certainly **no one cure** for the conditions we have been talking about—but then this is also true of chronic medical problems like rheumatoid arthritis or asthma. However, there are different sorts of treatment available that together can help relieve both schizophrenia and manic depressive illness, either wholly or in part. Treatment may take the form of medication, individual therapy aimed at helping people to understand how to manage their problems better and to arrange their lives in less stressful and more productive patterns, or family work that aims to help carers cope more effectively with difficulties. Selecting the best combination of such treatments is often a complicated business that calls for much thought on the part of the health professionals involved. We will take you through these issues at much greater length in Chapter 5.

As we have suggested already, the **outlook** for mental illness varies: some attacks last for days, weeks or months; others, for years or a lifetime. But even in the most prolonged conditions, there are variations in severity and periods when the sufferer is relatively well.

People who have suffered an attack of mania or depression usually get better, but as many as 10 per cent of those with the more severe forms do not. Although they may never have another attack, most will do so, usually after some years. Some sufferers, perhaps as many as 25 per cent, may have minor mood swings between attacks which can impair their efficiency. Attacks that come on gradually are likely to improve relatively slowly, and an illness that begins in later life hasn't such a good outlook.

However, having someone else in the family who also suffers from affective illness gives no clue as to outcome.

In general, the prospect for schizophrenia is less promising, but even here 25 per cent have only **a single attack** from which they recover completely. When we wrote the first edition of this book, only one person in ten was still in hospital five years after a first bout of schizophrenia. This figure is now lower still, although many of those who in the past would have stayed in hospital for a long time are now in hostels and nursing homes with a high degree of support. However, over half of those who develop schizophrenia do suffer quite considerable **continuing disability**, or have repeated attacks, usually not doing so well in life as they otherwise might have done. By 'disability' here we mean that sufferers are unable to do enough—looking after themselves, working, socialising—to lead as full and as happy a life as they might otherwise have done. Some may be quite disabled—a very few to the extent that they have to stay permanently in hospital, or in very highly supported housing.

The prospect for schizophrenia is better for those who do not have a family history of the illness. A relatively abrupt onset is also a good sign, particularly if it follows some kind of sudden stress. **Negative symptoms** (see p. 28) indicate a relatively bad outlook, mainly because they will probably persist when the acute symptoms have gone.

From what we have said so far, you will gather that it is often impossible at the beginning of a severe mental illness to predict what is going to happen later on. Professionals frequently avoid forthright opinions at this stage, mainly because they are frightened that what they say may turn out later to have been misleadingly optimistic, or pessimistic. Your relative will be offered one or more of various treatments, and these will affect the outcome in various ways and to a varying extent. Obviously, his or her circumstances, reactions, and ability to manage will influence the success of the treatment given. Certainly, considerable time may be needed, and it can be months or even years before improvements become apparent. All psychiatric professionals work within this sort of time span. It can be confusing and unnerving for both you and the sufferer to find that, unlike in physical illness, rapid improvements may not be expected.

2 Coping with Mental Illness

The problems you may have to deal with

Some of you will be fortunate: your mentally ill relative will recover and the family will gradually get over the turmoil. But if this does not happen or if your relative recovers but becomes ill again, then living with him or her may give rise to a variety of problems. As well as all the ordinary difficulties that families can face, there are extra ones, often unrecognised or poorly understood, that can arise because of a severe mental illness. The relatively new developments in **community care** (see Chapter 3) mean that families are now expected to cope at home at an earlier stage in the illness than was the case thirty years ago. The average mental hospital stay is now around three weeks, and almost all patients are discharged within a year. In many cases, in-patient hospital care is not felt necessary and people remain at home all the time.

Relatives often want to be involved in the recovery process, and in providing continuing support if necessary. In the past, unfortunately, they have often felt that they themselves have not been helped, that their requests for advice have been ignored and that problems have not been considered until a crisis has emerged. We believe that this situation used to arise because health professionals tended to see relatives simply as part of the client's environment, rather than as people with needs of their own. The Community Care Act of 1992 specified that carers should be consulted and included in care plans, so that relatives are now much more visible and central to care planning than in the past.

The Mental Health (Patients in the Community) Act (1995) that came into force in April 1996 now specifies that carers themselves have needs and are entitled in their own right to an assessment of these by the social services. This new Act should also make a difference to how carers are seen by the services.

After-effects of the illness

There is still considerable confusion between problems caused by the illness itself and its possible unseen after-effects, and those caused by **other factors**, such as the individual's character and reaction to what has happened, or the effects of medication. Because of this, it can be extremely difficult for you to get the balance right—for instance, between expecting too much of your relative and not expecting enough, or between allowing unreasonable behaviour to continue and blaming your relative for behaviour that he or she cannot control.

In one family, for example, one son, twenty-one-year-old Tony, had developed schizophrenia, and it was very difficult for the other members of the family—mother, successfully working brother and stepfather—to know what to expect. He had already changed from an active teenager with a talent for art into someone who was suspicious, sometimes violent, and very unwilling to get out of bed. When some of the more dramatic symptoms diminished in hospital and he returned home, he was still very uninterested in doing anything, difficult to talk to, and liable to lie in bed all day. The family either tended to think that he had been prescribed too much medication, which made them angry with the hospital, or, less charitably, they said he was just lazy and got very angry with him. In fact, some of Tony's loss of interest and tiredness was due not to medication or to personality but to the illness itself. This is very common when someone has had schizophrenia. It took a long time for the family to realise this, and to understand that although Tony was responsible for some of his behaviour, other aspects of it were beyond his control and he needed time and encouragement to become more active and more like his old self. In fact, it took about a year and a lot of family effort for him to re-establish a routine and get himself a part-time job.

This is a complex issue, and it does often take time to make the right adjustments. It will be a considerable while, as in Tony's case, before some individuals regain their former interest in the outside world. Indeed, a few never seem to do so. One woman described her daughter as 'losing her sparkle'.

The mother lived with her thirty-year-old daughter, Rachel. She had been very worried at the changes in her daughter at the start of her illness, as Rachel had a particular idea that she looked unacceptable to the outside world, and refused to go out. With hospital admission and treatment this idea faded, and Rachel returned home and was able to go out with her mother. However, she seemed to have lost her enthusiasm and spontaneity, and unless her mother made suggestions she would stay indoors doing very little all day. After some months some of the interest came back, but it was a very gradual process.

As already mentioned, a relative who has had a severe mental illness may also show much less in the way of facial expression and affection for the family and be harder to talk to. This can be both puzzling and hurtful; but it need not mean that your relative feels less deeply, just that his feelings are not expressed in the same open way. One father described it thus: 'You never know what they're thinking. He sits there all day and you'd think he'd be bored; he doesn't seem to be, but he never says.'

In this family the son, while retaining some odd ideas about others disliking him, was able to go to a day centre, but was rather uncommunicative for most of the time. He would accept food and having his laundry done for him, but answered in monosyllables and never expressed gratitude or seemed at all curious about his parents' viewpoint, or how they might have been upset over his illness.

Another problem is **unpredictability**. There may be some days when a patient is 'her old self', and then quite suddenly the carer says, 'I've lost her again.' These mood changes may occur without warning, so that an ordinary conversation can turn into a sudden series of accusations without apparent reason. Severe mental illnesses can affect people in this way, and the individual is often not in control of these strong feelings that suddenly become convictions. It is usually best to be aware that it can happen and to recognise it when it does. You should not feel that you have caused the switch of mood. The best strategy in the circumstances is normally to change the subject, distract your relative or leave him or her alone for a while. One family, whenever their daughter started a tirade against 'the Russians', would offer to make a cup of tea instead of pursuing an argument.

The after-effects of a severe mental illness can include loss of energy, sleeping a lot, spending time doing nothing and wanting to avoid people. Although it may look like it, you should not be tempted to see this just as laziness and unfriendliness but try to understand that it *is* an after-effect. If an individual does nothing else **at all** but sit in his or her own room, this can be harmful. In such cases, your relative should be encouraged to go out, to join in with some other family activities (even in silence), or to try going to a day centre if one is available. That a certain amount of time should be spent alone, even if he or she appears completely unoccupied, is not, however, surprising, and other family members should intrude on this only gently and with caution. It is probably best to encourage the individual to participate, and to help with some household chores, without demanding that these be done instantly or expecting too high a standard. Expectations can be gradually increased as competence and interest return.

When a lack of energy and a reluctance to be with people leads an individual with a mental illness to stay in bed in the mornings, relatives often find the situation difficult to deal with, being uncertain of the right approach. One mother found it useful and effective to offer cups of tea at regular intervals, together with a time check. She did *not* take up her daughter's breakfast, which remained on the table downstairs. Another mother adopted a more active approach. After calling her son several times, if he had not got up by midmorning she would go into his room. Then she would laughingly ask, 'Head first or feet first?', and physically pull him out of bed. At that point he would give in and get dressed.

Unacceptable or embarrassing behaviour

While families vary in their tolerance, there are several sorts of behaviour they are likely to find unacceptable. For example, some people might shout, swear or talk to themselves in a rather obvious manner, damage furniture or other objects, or threaten to harm themselves or others. Obviously, you will want to control behaviour like this, but you may feel unsure about the best way to do so without causing worse arguments or upsets. You may feel that you get no advice on this problem from doctors, social workers, or your relative's **key worker** (see p. 65): this is a common complaint. In all such circumstances, try to remain **calm**. Becoming upset or angry will make things worse. It can be helpful to remember that your relative is not and was not always like this, and may not be aware of exactly how hurtful or upsetting such behaviour is. People may well react in this way because they are actually very **angry** or **frightened**. Waiting until a particular outburst is over, and then saying, 'I know you've been upset—what can I do to help?' has been found useful by others faced with this problem. It may be a good idea to leave the room, or to suggest that your relative goes to his or her own room or to another for a while. One young man would often talk and swear to himself. The family managed to limit this by making it a rule that it should only happen in his bedroom.

It is often a good idea, after a particularly upsetting or embarrassing event, for the whole family, including the sick person, to talk about it and work out ways of avoiding or limiting similar situations in the future. It is much better for all concerned if, when everyone is calm, you can make it clear to each other exactly what can be tolerated and what will not be, rather than leaving things unsaid and letting irritation and upset build up.

Peter was in his early thirties, and sometimes when severely ill he would take his clothes off, regardless of who else was in the room. His mother and married sister, who lived with him, would ask him afterwards why he had done this and would tell him how upsetting it was for them. Peter said that sometimes he felt he was told to undress as an act of penitence, but agreed eventually to do it in private whenever possible. He needed reminding, but this worked reasonably well and was easier than coping with his behaviour or explaining it to visitors.

Coping with a depressed relative

If you live with someone who is mentally ill, maintaining the relationship while he or she is depressed can be one of the hardest things to manage. Depression saps the sufferer's will, and is quite capable of sapping yours too. It can be particularly exasperating to see your best efforts to help come to naught, and it is not surprising that many relatives give up trying and withdraw—emotionally, at any rate. Unfortunately, this reinforces the individual's sense of guilt and poor opinion of his- or herself. It also emphasises how isolating depression can be.

However, although it may often be difficult, there *are* things you can do. The approach will differ according to whether your relative is just becoming depressed, or whether the depression has really got a grip.

In the early stages, it may be possible to improve things by using the sorts of approach that would be helpful for someone who was distressed or unhappy in the ordinary way. You may have to take the initiative, though, because depressed people sometimes find it hard to confide. You can help by providing sympathy and sensible advice. For instance, if things at work are difficult, you may be able to see a way through the problems that has not occurred to your relative, or use persuasion to have them put to one side until he or she is in a better position to deal with them. You may be able to provide practical support, reducing the load on your relative by temporarily taking on some task or responsibility. One of the adverse effects of depression is to give the individual a distorted view of things, which in turn reinforces the depression. By talking things through with him or her you may be able to provide the other person with a healthier perspective.

Reassurance is important to depressed people, but it must not be offered in a crude way. It is *not* reassuring to have one's fears and worries dismissed; it just makes one feel that the other person has not understood, or doesn't believe that the distress is real or valid. It is much better to listen to the basis of those worries, to take them seriously and then to spot where your relative is being unrealistic or oversensitive and put forward an alternative view. Your interest and concern will also help to give reassurance of the thing that your relative is very unsure of—that is, his or her worth.

When people are depressed, others often feel they might try and take them out of themselves. To this end they may suggest various social activities, or even a holiday. Unfortunately, this is often not a good idea, and in any case must be done very carefully. If it doesn't work and the individual does not enjoy the occasion, it may heighten his or her sense of impairment and the depression may increase as a result. The sufferer may also feel guilty about spoiling things for others. Any social activity must therefore be planned in the light of the individual's state of mind. Simple visits by relatives or close friends may be all he or she can take and benefit from at this stage.

If your efforts to get your relative over his or her depression do not succeed within a week or two, enlist medical help, at first through your family doctor; and, if necessary, press for psychiatric help. If there is a history of depressive illness, you may be quite a good judge of when things have gone too far, although it is often difficult to steer a course between tardiness and haste.

Even if your relative is getting assistance and medication from the professionals, there are still things you can do to help. Indeed, it is important that you are not seen to give up in your attempts. Given that depressed people are rather unrewarding to be with, there must always be a temptation for you to withdraw—and you may *have* to have some time on your own just in order to keep going. As a result of their doubts about and poor opinion of their worth some depressed people can be rather clinging and dependent, and this can also be difficult.

There may come a point when a depressed person cannot actually manage his or her responsibilities any more. When this has been reached, it is really up to you to assume these responsibilities yourself or organise others to do so. This means that you must take charge and take over all household decisions, without negotiation. Depressed people may be very **indecisive**. This may lead to long discussions about trivial matters that get nowhere because they continually change the basis of their argument. Avoid such pointless disputes, or at least try to defer them. Sometimes individuals become very opinionated about family matters, and this too may cause long arguments that fail to produce constructive solutions.

Taking over in this way may make your depressed relative feel very guilty at the burden he or she is placing on you. You can manage this by explaining that it is only a temporary arrangement, that when he or she is better—but not before—you will expect your relative to take things on once again, and that he or she would help you in the same way if the circumstances were reversed. Depressed people often feel safer if they can feel that someone has taken firm control of the situation. You need a certain skill to recognise the point at which you really have to take over. If you delay too long you may cause your relative a lot of unnecessary anguish. If you rush in, you may be encouraging him or her to give up more than is necessary.

In any case, even if you are doing most of the important things, you should still encourage the sufferer to do something, even though it may not seem worth the trouble it causes you.

Anne and her husband lived with her father Bob, who became depressed. Even though it was as much as he could manage, she still got him to dry the dishes. He could only do this very slowly and under close supervision, but Anne still thought it was important that he should do it. It gave her something to thank him for, and it allowed him the feeling of a task done.

Another example of the use of a simple activity to help someone who is depressed is given on p. 117.

If your relative has become so depressed that he or she cannot do anything at all, you must consider whether the person shouldn't be in hospital. You certainly must not hide the situation from the doctor—indeed, you should make arrangements to discuss it with him or her.

In the vast majority of cases, depressed mood is temporary, so if you can last it out things *will* get better. Very occasionally, depression may take the form of long-lasting misery that seems unaffected by treatment. This is very difficult indeed to live with, and sometimes the only way to manage is to arrange matters in less than ideal ways. This might include taking over your relative's responsibilities, not on a temporary, but on a permanent basis. And it requires that you deliberately protect yourself from your relative's misery, at least for part of the time, by organising your life away from him or her to some extent. These courses of action will not do much to improve the sufferer's mood, but at least they may enable you to continue looking after him or her, and yourself.

Coping with delusions

One of the most difficult problems you might have to face would occur if your sick relative had a fixed belief such as 'The television is talking to me.' If you deny the truth of a belief like this, you may be seen to have joined 'them'. If you go along with it, the belief may become even more fixed in the individual's mind. You will find that **arguing** is **not** helpful. A useful strategy is for you to agree that the person believes what he or she says, while making it clear that the experience is not real for you. 'I know you think the TV is talking to you—you are sensitive to that sort of thing at times. I don't find it talks to me', is one way of drawing a line between *his or her* reality and the outside world.

Michael's wife could not at first understand what her husband was saying when he told her that he was convinced that he had a special mission to fulfil. While accepting that he felt such urgency and sympathising with him, she made it clear that it was not a belief she held, and that it was more important to her to have some help with a specific task (looking after their young son). This combination of sympathy—it is very important not to be dismissive—and distraction was successful some of the time in calming Michael and helping him not to act on his belief.

Sometimes, if you have a good relationship with your relative, reviewing with him or her the evidence for a particular belief can be helpful. **This is not the same as trying to prove someone wrong.** It is not something to argue about. We do know that once any of us has a strong belief, be it about politics, religion or world events, it is very common not to look closely at the evidence for another point of view. So particularly if your relative has a *distressing* belief, looking for 'disconfirming' evidence together and reviewing it dispassionately can actually help to reassure and reduce upset.

At times Peter thought that he was evil, and that if he was watching the news on TV he could cause the next disaster that was reported. He often felt he knew what was going to be said next and that these thoughts then influenced world events, causing bad things to happen. Because he felt he was responsible for this, he often thought he should kill himself. His sister had tried to discuss these ideas with him, but he was always totally convinced that his thoughts were the cause. Then, one lunchtime, by discussing just beforehand what Peter thought was going to be on the news, they were both able to sit and watch it and see if Peter's worst fears were confirmed or not. Peter had known that a terrible Third World disaster was imminent, but in fact the news that day was about a political scandal. Suggesting to Peter that what he thought did not always happen helped to reassure him that he was not always to blame. It was not something he had been able to do for himself, but the discussion with his sister beforehand had helped to relieve his distress. Peter began to see for himself that his worst forebodings did not inevitably come true and to reassure himself to some extent.

Discussing the evidence for a specific belief has to be done sympathetically and carefully, or it can make the sufferer feel more convinced than ever. If you do try this sort of approach, you must be able to abandon it if it is clearly being unhelpful or distressing, and try to reassure and distract the person instead—'It's all right, we don't have to talk about it if you don't want to'—and then change the subject. It may in the end be as helpful to switch off the news, or suggest another activity, if discussion is not possible with your relative at that moment.

Restlessness, overactivity and anxiety

Some clients, particularly those with severe **depression**, can become extremely restless, uncomfortable and upset. They may be unable to sit still or to sleep, and spend hours pacing the room. No amount of reassurance seems to make any difference. You may well find this behaviour almost unbearable if it continues for long. It is nearly always helpful to acknowledge to your relative that **he or she** can't feel very comfortable or happy or relaxed, either. Sometimes a walk outside together will be helpful; sometimes, separate walks outside will be more so! Fortunately, symptoms of this type almost invariably get better as the illness recedes.

Pat, a mother of two in her forties, would sometimes feel unbearably anxious and upset, and ask constantly for reassurance that 'it was not her fault' and that she was not shouting obscenities. This was very difficult for her family to tolerate, as indeed it was for the staff when she went to hospital, because reassurance did no more than help her temporarily, and the feelings could last for days at a time. The best solution seemed to be to offer a brief stock phrase of reassurance, rather than to spend a long time trying to comfort her, and again to offer alternatives or distraction. Comments like 'We know how upset you are—try to sit down and watch TV/read the paper' seemed to be helpful while this distressing behaviour was at its height.

Effects on sexual relationships

Those of you who are married to or cohabiting with someone who becomes severely mentally ill will be concerned about **sexual aspects** of the relationship. While they are ill, many people, particularly those with severe depression, will lose much of their sexual desire and interest. Some types of drug treatment also tend to reduce sexual interest. This, together with a loss of more general expressions of affection, can be particularly difficult for partners to understand or accept.

When the illness improves, sexual and general interest will probably return. You may, however, find that the relationship has been changed in sexual and other ways, and that new patterns must be established. Or you may find that your feelings have changed irrevocably, and believe that the partnership cannot survive. All the partners we have talked to in this situation have wanted to end the relationship at one time or another, although the guilt that this produces can be equally unbearable. Divorce is no longer uncommon in our society, and for some relationships a severe mental illness is a final strain that cannot be tolerated. Some couples, on the other hand, find that such experiences draw them closer together than they have been before.

Carol and her husband Bill were in their fifties but had not been married long. When Bill developed a late-onset type of schizophrenia, they found it very difficult at first to adjust. He had always had trouble staying in jobs, but this problem suddenly became much worse after a particularly damaging row with his boss, following which he refused to leave the house and was very disturbed. Eventually, after treatment in hospital, he returned home, and they had to decide how their relationship ought to continue. Carol's first impulse was to give up her career to 'look after Bill'. Bill didn't want her to do this, and felt she would resent it in the long run. Finally, they decided that Carol should continue working part-time while Bill began to take on some of the domestic responsibilities instead of trying and failing at jobs. Bill's new role took some time to establish, but he began to enjoy it and gained a sense of achievement from having dinner ready for a tired spouse. Carol was actually very glad to relinquish the housework, and also to have time to spend with him on days when she was not at work. In the end they both described the relationship as very close, and as more fulfilling, including sexually, in the way it had developed.

Promiscuity as a problem

Particularly if you have a daughter, you may be worried by the **promiscuous behaviour** that develops in some mentally ill people. A much loved child, who may have been shy before the illness began, may seem to lose discrimination and choose as sexual partners people who would previously have been considered as unlikely or unsuitable in some way. Sometimes you will feel particularly concerned because your daughter appears vulnerable to sexual advances, and you may worry that outsiders could be taking advantage. This can be a very upsetting problem: you find that your normal acceptance of an adult's desire for independence and sexual freedom conflicts with your wish to protect a loved child from sexual abuse or hurt. For adults with mental illness, there is rarely any way to enforce sexual rules. Even though you dislike it, you may have to accept a certain amount of independence and sexual freedom. The most useful approach is to **support** relatives through these relationships, showing you still care, despite their acting in ways you would not choose them to. Help with **contraception** and advice about safe sex is usually relevant and important, and you may be the person best able to suggest and organise this.

Most families, particularly parents, find it very difficult to accept this side of their sick relatives' adult life.

The parents of Jane, a woman in her early thirties, were distressed by her going off for several nights with an unknown man, after which she had returned home dishevelled and uncommunicative. They never did hear the full details of this episode. Thereafter they tended to be rather protective of her, and discouraged male friends from phoning or calling round. Jane herself was not worried by her lack of a steady boyfriend, and she did not disagree with her parents' attitude. It can be much more difficult if this kind of situation becomes an area of dispute in your family, because it has to be sorted out in some way that respects your relative's adult needs.

In some cases, promiscuity may be apparent for only some of the time. This can happen in **mania** where it might be an early sign of relapse, and you may need to enlist urgent professional help. We give advice on how to do this on pp. 46–52.

Diet

There is no good evidence that **dietary factors** can cause schizophrenia or manic depressive illness. Psychiatric disorders do result from deficiencies of **vitamins**, but these are quite different and, in addition, can often be recognised by their effects on the sufferer's physical health. However, many psychiatric patients do have poor appetites, and it is important to ensure as far as possible that they have **a good diet**, containing the essential nutrients.

On the other hand, some people with mental illness **eat too much**, and this can be a problem if they are also rather under-active, which is sometimes the case. In addition, individuals taking major tranquillisers, antidepressants or lithium may be liable to put on weight. It is not good for someone with a mental illness, any more than it is for anyone else, to get too fat. If this is the case with your relative, encourage him or her to lose weight, although this may not always be very feasible, as well as appearing to be the least of the problems. Sometimes the doctor may be able to change the person's drugs for ones that are less fattening, and it can be helpful to ask about this if you think it is a problem.

Self-care

This is not a problem for everyone with these illnesses. However, for some, the illness or its after-effects lead to a loss of interest in how they look and how they look after themselves. In extreme cases, self-neglect may be severe, with the individual not eating properly and living in squalor. This is not usually allowed to happen, though, if he or she lives with a relative! Nevertheless, there are often day-to-day problems over bathing or shaving, and there may be a difficulty about changing clothes, particularly underwear. One mother described how her son became attached to a particular set of clothes he had on and would not change them. All she could do was to persuade him to bath about once a month, and to wash these clothes while he was doing so. When eventually they wore out, the same thing happened to the new set.

It is helpful in such circumstances to establish family ground rules for a *minimal* routine of bathing, laundering, changing of sheets—one that you can all at any rate *tolerate*. Once a week may be a reasonable target, and, once it has been negotiated, encourage your relative to stick to it. It can be useful to decide on a particular convenient day and include bathing as part of a general routine of getting up, getting dressed and getting out of the house. It may well need your practical help to start off with, as shaving or hair-washing may be particularly burdensome for a person feeling very preoccupied or unwell.

Use of alcohol
While there is no intrinsic reason why a person who has had a severe mental illness cannot drink alcohol, there may be several reasons why it is inadvisable. First, anyone taking drugs such as the major tranquillisers needs to be aware that they interact with alcohol. This can **exaggerate** the normal effects of alcohol, and the individual may quickly become sleepy or morose, or less in control of strong emotions such as anger or fear.

Doctors normally recommend that anyone on psychiatric drugs should drink very little alcohol, if indeed any at all. However, this may be quite unrealistic. Your relative may greatly resent being given 'rules' about drinking, whether by professionals or by you yourself, and may rightly feel that alcohol is the only pleasure he or she now enjoys. In general, a couple of pints of beer or two or three glasses of wine every other day should not cause too many problems. As a rule of thumb, the individual should try to think of his or her drugs as doubling the potency of alcohol, so the effect of a pint of beer is likely to equal that of two pints in former times. It may be that a little cautious experimenting is required—as with the rest of us, some mentally ill people have much more control over their alcohol consumption than others. Calm discussion about the problems that excessive use of alcohol can cause for your relative and for other members of the family is probably the best starting-point. If alcohol *is* causing serious problems, the team concerned with your relative's care should be told about it, in case he or she is not admitting these problems to them.

Some families—fortunately, not a majority—find that worrying about a relative's alcohol consumption and his or her resulting behaviour can be one of the worst aspects of the illness. The person may well not drink to what would normally be regarded as excess, but because even small amounts of alcohol can have effects when combined with drugs, the results of quite moderate drinking can be very unpleasant.

Malcolm lived with his mother, and would nag and worry her every night for money for a few beers. He would consume these, and then return home drunk and be sick over the bed. It took a lot of negotiation between Malcolm, his mother and the mental health team before this pattern changed and Malcolm could behave in a more acceptable manner. A different strategy was developed by Eric's mother. When he said he wanted a bottle of whisky, she would suggest that they both needed a drink and offer to buy one on her next shopping trip. She would do this, and for a few nights afterwards they had a couple of drinks together. After that Eric lost interest, and the bottle remained half-full in the cupboard.

Substance abuse

As well as alcohol, taking illicit drugs is one of the leisure activities of increasing numbers of people, particularly when they are in their teens and twenties. Cannabis, E, amphetamines and LSD may be used, as may heroin, cocaine or 'crack'. While there is some argument about causes and effects, such drugs, particularly if taken frequently, at the very least intensify the problems of someone with a psychotic illness, and often seem to set off another attack. People who become dependent on a particular illicit drug, such as heroin or amphetamines, may also find that they acquire all the associated problems, such as having to find the money needed to get the drugs, and becoming less and less concerned with anything else while they search for the next fix.

Recent research on heavy users, whether of street drugs or of alcohol, who also have psychosis suggests that they have even more frequent emergencies and other difficulties. Substance abuse is likely to need help in its own right, separately from the problem of schizophrenia or severe depression. Because of this, you may well need to be aware of the possibility of this happening to your relative, if substance abuse is one of his or her difficulties, and be ready to contact your GP for specialist advice on the drug or alcohol question. Unfortunately, as with all addictions, the only way to help the person is to lead them to recognise that they themselves need to change, and this may take many years of disaster and heartache. Such combined problems are some of the most difficult to deal with. If you are in this position, try to obtain all the help you can, both for your relative and for yourself. But you may also need to recognise that there are limits to what you can do.

Suicide threats

Schizophrenia and manic depressive illness are associated with a higher than average risk of attempted or actual **suicide**. Sometimes suicidal feelings may be a near-rational response to hopeless circumstances, but in other cases there may be no apparent cause. One of the reasons why the mental health team may suggest a hospital admission is to reduce the risk of suicide and help such feelings recede. Sometimes people are most at risk of attempting suicide when there has been some initial improvement. They may feel a bit more energetic, but still believe that they are a burden to others, that they have nothing to live for and that the future is completely bleak. It is not possible to prevent all suicide attempts: a determined individual can often be successful, even when under apparently close surveillance in a home, a hostel or a hospital ward.

Fred, a depressed middle-aged man, was being monitored in hospital because he was regarded as a suicide risk. He said he wanted to use the toilet, but while he was there the nurse watching him was called briefly to a disturbance on the ward. Although he was only gone a moment, when he returned Fred had thrown himself from the toilet window, three floors up.

Threats of suicide can be very upsetting and difficult to deal with. It is commonly said that people who talk frequently about suicide never actually try to kill themselves. This is **not true**, and **all threats of suicide should be taken seriously**. It is true that people sometimes make such threats for effect or because it is the only way they can communicate how distressed they are. At other times they most certainly are seriously intent on killing themselves, and you may find it impossible to tell one kind of threat from another. It is sensible to take elementary **precautions**, such as not leaving tablets lying around the house and informing the mental health team if the sufferer seems more than normally tearful, morose or hopeless. You may find it helpful to ask your relative how he or she is feeling—sometimes it is just necessary to notice the sadness and attempt to offer comfort and reassurance, if it can be accepted. An arm around the shoulders or a cuddle may sometimes be easier than words, and often more effective.

Dealing with emergencies

It is in the nature of severe mental illness that you may sometimes be called upon to deal with urgent situations. The appropriate management of these depends on the exact circumstances.

Probably the most common situation is when you become

aware that your relative is rapidly deteriorating or **relapsing**. It is always possible, and often appropriate, to seek the advice of your family doctor when this happens. You may be able to persuade your relative to make an appointment, and it will be helpful if you can go too. Sometimes, individuals may decline to see the doctor. This may be because they have particular fears about what may happen—for instance, that they will have to go into hospital, perhaps never to come out, or that they will be 'sectioned' (see p. 124) and taken to hospital involuntarily. If they are reluctant, try to find out what they feel about going to see the GP—you may be able to reassure them and get them to change their mind, particularly if you offer to go with them. But if you are completely unable to get them to visit the surgery, it is reasonable for you to make an appointment and see the GP yourself. If you decide that this is necessary, there is plainly no point in doing it half-heartedly—you must put your doctor clearly in the picture. Otherwise, he or she may feel that you have just come for reassurance. The GP may make a home visit if it seems reasonable to do so from what you tell him or her.

If your relative is currently attending a psychiatric out-patient department, the best procedure may be to consult the psychiatrist involved by phone. He or she may be in a position to reassure you. But if a genuine crisis is developing, he or she can suggest the best course of action, whether this may be a temporary increase in medication or even hospital admission. Usually your relative will be receiving visits from a **community psychiatric nurse**, or whichever member of the mental health team is the **key worker** (see p. 65). These two will nearly always know your relative better than the psychiatrist does. In these circumstances, it is sensible to contact the key worker, who may decide to make an urgent visit to assess the situation. Key workers should routinely provide instructions about how best to contact them, and if at all possible you should ensure you know how to do this *before* a crisis arises. In cases of doubt, the consultant psychiatrist's secretary will usually know how to get a message to them.

In some circumstances you may feel it is sufficient for the sufferer's next appointment to be brought forward. This can usually be done, either through the appointments secretary at the hospital or by phoning the mental health team.

Not all patients need to remain in contact with psychiatric

out-patient services. It is usually appropriate for relatives of those showing signs of relapse or deterioration after a long period of good health to approach the family doctor, particularly if they have moved house since last receiving treatment. Mental hospitals tend to have rigid **catchment areas**, and those who have moved outside the area of their previous hospital will come under the psychiatric services of their new area of residence. In such cases, it is essential to proceed through the GP. Family doctors prefer patients to visit them in their surgery, as this is usually the most effective way for them of using their time. However, for some psychiatric patients this may be inappropriate, so it may sometimes be in order to ask your GP to visit your relative at home. He or she may, after seeing the patient, decide to arrange **hospital admission** immediately. However, an **out-patient appointment** to see a consultant in the new hospital may be made. If the sufferer is unwilling or unable to attend, or should be seen quickly, your family doctor may invite a consultant to visit him or her at home (a **domiciliary visit**). Social services departments now have a **legal duty** to arrange for an assessment if a relative writes to the director.

Occasionally, your relative may become very acutely disturbed, and where there are warning signs of this it is obviously better to take action early rather than late. Sometimes people deteriorate very rapidly indeed, and you may need to act immediately. If you have a particularly good relationship with the hospital consultant, an admission can sometimes be arranged by contacting him or her directly. Otherwise, it may be necessary to obtain the services of the GP, who can assess the situation in the home and arrange a necessary admission accordingly. If such an urgent situation arises when you and the sick person are away from home, you may need to enlist the help of a local GP, who to start with may in turn arrange admission to a nearby hospital. The patient can then be transferred to his or her own local hospital when it is convenient and practicable.

In a few areas there are **special crisis intervention centres**, where you can go for help without necessarily contacting your family doctor. In a few psychiatric hospitals—for instance, the Maudsley Hospital in London—there are twenty-four-hour walk-in emergency clinics, which will provide an initial assessment, offer advice and possibly arrange admission to a local hospital. In an emergency clinic, you and your sick relative are likely to have to wait for some time before being seen, as they run them on a 'first come, first served' basis. It is probably not a good idea to go to a general hospital casualty department with a purely psychiatric problem. If possible, find out beforehand from your local mental health team what you should do in an out-of-hours emergency, and keep the relevant contact numbers easily available. If you are seriously worried about your safety or that of your relative and it is an emergency, **phone 999 and ask for the police.**

Sometimes people are so disturbed that they deny that they have become unwell. In these circumstances, they may need compulsory admission to prevent them from harming themselves or others. This has to be arranged through the GP. Details of the legal involvement of the carer in the procedures of compulsory admission are given in Chapter 6.

If your very disturbed relative leaves the house and you are seriously worried, it may be reasonable to inform the local police. They can act under the **1983 Mental Health Act** or the Scottish or Northern Irish equivalents to bring a person suffering from a mental illness who is likely to be a danger to themselves or others to a **place of safety** (see p. 127).

The final emergency you may have to face arises from a **suicide** attempt.

Most such attempts these days involve self-poisoning. Not all are equally serious, but you should seek medical help if there is **any possibility at all** that your relative could have swallowed more than the usual dose of a drug, or that he or she could retain an intention to end his or her life. Some drugs like paracetamol (Panadol) can be fatal after a delay, even though they appear to have no immediate effects. In the case of any overdose, you should seek general medical, rather than psychiatric, help. Family doctors usually do not have adequate facilities for dealing with overdosage, although they can help to assess the severity of the overdose and advise whether the patient needs to be taken to hospital. So if there is any suspicion that the overdose might be a dangerous one, either take your relative to a **casualty department** or phone 999 for an **ambulance**.

Until the ambulance comes you are in charge of the situation, and this means at the very least that you must keep a **close watch**.

After all, if your relative is conscious, it is possible that he or she intends to try again. If you don't already know, try to find out what the person has taken, by asking and by checking the labels of any bottles or other containers. A drink will help to dilute the poison and ease any damage to the stomach. Try water, milk or barley water. Do **not** give salt drinks: they aren't very good at bringing on vomiting, and they can themselves act as a poison.

It is more important to get your relative to hospital as quickly as possible than to make him or her vomit. However, after you have given a drink it may be reasonable to try to make the person sick. **Only do this if your relative is conscious and cooperative.** Do **not** do it if the poison is a **corrosive** (bleach, strong acid or alkali). The way to induce vomiting is by rubbing the back of the throat either with your fingers or with the blunt end of a spoon wrapped in a handkerchief.

When the ambulance arrives and you have a good idea what your relative has taken, make sure that any container goes to hospital as well. Label it and give it to the ambulance driver. If you have managed to make your relative vomit, try to collect a sample of the vomit to send with the ambulance, again labelled, so that it can be analysed.

If your relative becomes unconscious, try to put him or her into the **recovery position** (see the drawing opposite). This is necessary because he or she may choke if left lying face up—saliva or vomit could flow back into the windpipe and block it, or the tongue could fall back and block the throat. If breathing is obviously difficult, run your finger round the inside of the mouth to remove any obstruction (including false teeth). Then move the head gently back and keep it there so that the tongue is brought clear of the throat. Now turn your relative into the recovery position. Lying on his or her side in this way will keep the airway clear and allow any fluid in the mouth to flow out. Before placing the sufferer in this position, make sure there is nothing in the pockets that might be uncomfortable to lie on. Cover your relative loosely with a blanket or coat.

- As apparently unconscious people may be able to hear, be careful what you say.
- **Never give anything by mouth to anyone who is unconscious.** It may well choke him or her.

The Recovery Position

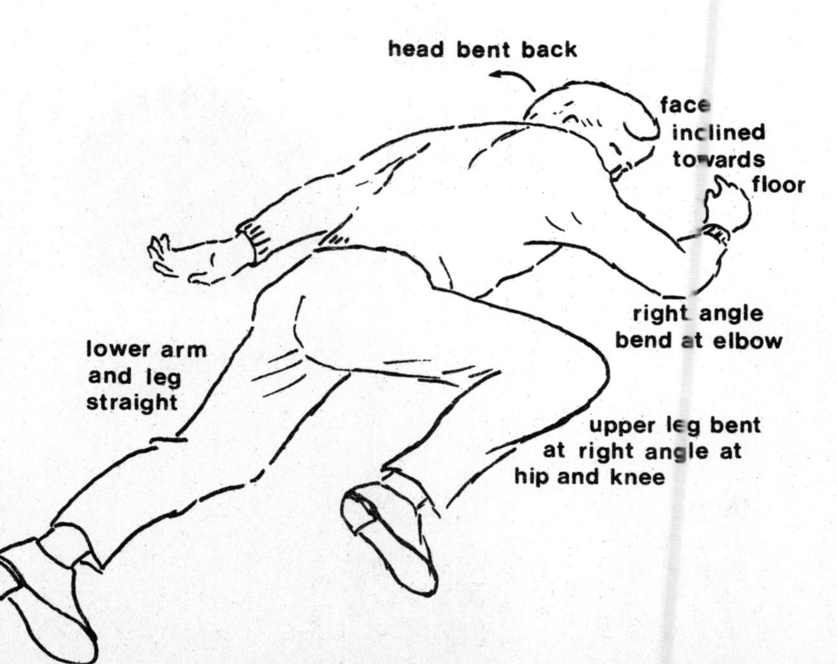

- The recovery position is also advisable for people who are feeling faint, and essential for those who might suddenly become unconscious.
- If your relative stops breathing, try artificial respiration if you know how to do it.

Coping with violent behaviour

We live in what is perhaps an increasingly violent society, but relatively few mentally ill people are in any way violent. It must be said, however, that the ones who are do get a lot of publicity. Nevertheless, despite its rarity, violence in the mentally ill does pose some rather special problems for the people who live with them.

The first thing to acknowledge about violence is that, like suicide, it is not always preventable. There are sometimes going to be situations where it erupts without anyone being able to do anything to stop it. In the worst possible case, a pattern of repeated violence may be so established—for instance, between a powerful adult son and his ageing frail mother—that it is not possible to change it. If this is the kind of situation you are in, it may be necessary for the two of you to stop living together, and even for you to take such actions as changing the locks or getting a court injunction against your relative.

However, things rarely get as bad as this, and action can usually be taken to deal with the violent behaviour. This action has three aspects, depending on whether it is to do with anticipating the violence, to do with the act itself, or to do with the aftermath.

Effective action taken **before** an individual behaves aggressively is obviously to be preferred. If you know that your sick relative is particularly irritable and therefore in a mood that may lead to violence, you may be able to avoid triggering it. One way of doing this is **simple avoidance**—keep out of his or her way, go to another room, go out for a walk or to the cinema. Sometimes you may have noticed that certain topics or situations tend to provoke anger, so avoid these if possible. The strategy of avoidance can be quite effective, but it may have the drawback that nothing in the situation ultimately changes, especially as it is not usually possible to keep on avoiding indefinitely. One woman learned to recognise when tension was building up in her son from the expression on his face. When this happened, she would keep quiet and leave the room. However, it was not always possible to stay out of the living-room, as it disturbed the domestic routine of the rest of the family.

A somewhat more subtle policy is **deflection**: if tension seems to be building up in your relative it may be possible to defuse it by suggesting some simple routine activity, such as going to the shops or doing some household chore. Clearly, this requires sensitivity and good judgement, as the wrong choice may make the situation worse. Sometimes relatives learn by experience that certain phrases are calming, and can be used to defuse the situation. One family would say, 'Why don't you go and have a lie down?' Sometimes this would work, but at other times the suggestion would be received angrily. It then worked better to say, 'Well, go out and buy *me* some cigarettes—here's the money—and come back when you feel calmer.'

A more direct approach is to confront your relative with his or her anger: this must be done **very gently**. One way of doing it is by saying in a quiet and neutral tone something like 'I can see you are upset. Won't you tell me what's the matter?' This may sound trite, but at least it gives him or her the chance of talking about the angry feelings, rather than necessarily acting on them. Again, this requires very fine judgement, but it also carries the possibility of sorting the situation out in a more basic and complete way.

Sometimes the individual may become violent because he or she has misinterpreted things. This may be the sort of misinterpretation that any of us can slip into but which those who are distressed may make more easily, or it may be the result of delusional ideas. In either case, if you realise that your relative is becoming angry as a result of the misinterpretation, you may be able to clarify the situation by gentle questioning. If the misinterpretation is not a delusional one, it may be possible for you to clear things up. If it *is* delusional, it may help to draw lines between the other person's reality and your own, or to look at the evidence together, in the manner suggested on p. 38.

However far you may get with clarifying misinterpretations, it is important to keep the transaction quiet and calm, using a firm and unflustered voice. If you can give the impression that you aren't going to become upset or angry, this will give him or her the feeling that things are under control, and this in turn will exert a calming influence. On some days one young woman would keep bursting in on her mother, shouting threateningly, 'I know you're trying to kill me. Why are you making me feel ill?' Her mother had learnt that one response that would calm her down was to say firmly but clearly, 'No, I was just sitting here reading the paper. Please don't shout.' It was often helpful to use distraction as well: 'Why don't we go out for a walk/make a cup of tea?'

Very often violence is a response to frustration—it can arise when you refuse something your relative wants. This may happen sometimes anyway, but it is more likely if the ground rules of your relationship have not been made very clear. So, for example, if you appear to have been inconsistent about what you think is all right and what not, violence may be the method that your relative uses to get you to permit what you would prefer to refuse. This underlines the importance of firmness and clarity in your relationship with someone who is severely mentally ill. He or she may be quite disturbed, but will still be able to recognise this firmness and realise that there are limits beyond which he or she cannot pass. Knowing the boundaries in this way may actually help your relative feel safer. Firmness in this context is not to be confused with bossiness or intrusiveness. 'We agreed how much money you should have each day. I can't give you any more', said with conviction, confidently and consistently when the agreed limit has been reached, is one example of the right sort of firmness.

But although consistency may be an ideal, it is not all that easy to achieve, particularly if the situation has been going on for a long time and you have not been able to get help and guidance. If you have been inconsistent in the past, the pattern may, sadly, be impossible to modify. Inconsistency in one member of the family coexisting with violence in another is a frequent cause of family break-up, although the relationship may stagger painfully on for a long time before this eventually happens. Usually when there *is* a break-up, the well individual feels extremely guilty, even though the decision was the only realistic and practicable one to take. In our experience, the relationship which most frequently gets locked into violence in this way is that between a mother, often elderly, and her ill but vigorous son; however, it can happen in most types of relationship—we also know, for instance, of caring husbands who have been at their wits' end and indeed intimidated by their wives' violence.

You may be quite skilful at managing your relationship with your mentally ill relative, and yet there are still times when he or she becomes violent with you. It is just not possible to be completely in control of the situation all the time. After all, professional staff are hit and hurt in other ways by patients from time to time; it can be a question of just being in the wrong place at the wrong time.

So how can you deal with the immediate threat or the fact of violence? It helps if you have thought out beforehand what you will do, and what you are prepared to do. It obviously depends to a major extent on how able you are physically to withstand an assault. The first principle is that, immediately you become aware that you might be about to be attacked, you avoid getting stuck in a corner of the room. Try to keep the furniture between you and your relative. Leave the room if necessary and if possible. If you can't get out, as a last resort use a chair or a blanket or jacket as a defence. You may need to leave the house and call or phone for help. It may be useful to have made an arrangement with a neighbour beforehand. Do not be afraid to call the police if necessary.

Unfortunately, people like social workers or the police may not be able to do very much before violence has actually occurred. This seems crazy, but it is, of course, the other side of our civil liberties in this country.

However, in response to your call the police will at least appear on the scene, and having several police officers around will frequently calm things down, even to the extent that when they have gone your relative does not become so angry again. This matter of calling the police does require judgement, though—and if you get to the stage where you are continually having to contend with outbursts of rage and violence and continually calling in the police, there is no longer any proper basis for your relationship. You must get outside advice urgently, preferably from a member of the psychiatric team involved in your relative's care, and if the circumstances cannot be changed for the better you must seriously consider parting company.

If, as sometimes happens, there is no escape or possibility of getting help, and the threat of violence is immediate and dangerous, you have to comply with doing things you don't want to. This is particularly the case if the individual has a knife or a gun, but also if he or she is much bigger and stronger than you.

If your relative has actually been violent towards you, hit you or whatever, it is important to try to deal with it **afterwards** in a way that may reduce the likelihood of a recurrence. It is relatively unusual to be badly hurt by a mentally ill person. All the same, being hit is often very upsetting even when the physical damage is slight, because it says something to you about your relationship and also about the future—that it may be unpleasant, violent and uncontrollable.

It is important that you should gently but firmly confront the individual with the fact that he or she has been violent and upset you. Do this later, when he or she has had time to settle down—perhaps the next day. Most acts of violence occur in the evening or at night time, and talking about it during daylight has a normalising effect. Point out that you were hurt and upset by the behaviour—he or she may not realise the effect it has had on you. Then try to get your relative to apologise—this makes it clear that he or she has gone beyond acceptable limits. At the same time, explore the incident and try to find out why it happened. Your relative may have been angry as a response to being very frightened, and your reassurance may be what is needed. Or he or she may have felt that you were being unreasonable in some way. You may be able to explain the situation and your view of it in a way that is reassuring. It may then be possible to resolve your differences. Perhaps he or she was triggered into violence by alcohol, substance abuse, or even lack of sleep. Pinpointing particular triggers can help avoid future episodes.

Finally, acts of violence often mean that the individual is relapsing, and this may require you to take further action (see p. 60).

Money problems

Some people with severe mental illness become very unrealistic about **money**, either during their illness or afterwards. This is particularly true of the **manic phases** of manic depressive illness, and some of you may realise that the illness is returning because the sufferer draws out large amounts of money and goes on a spending spree. Some people may not be able to get a job, and rely totally on social security or sickness benefit. They may find it impossible to budget, and demand extra money to pay for cigarettes, illicit drugs, alcohol or daily necessities. If this is so in your situation, you may find these demands difficult to refuse, but resent the fact that your relative cannot be more responsible or independent. Sometimes a **daily budget** can be organised with him or her, so that money is spaced out over the week and not spent all at once. Jane was able to agree with her mother that she should have £4 a day for herself. Clothing and other items were bought rarely, but out of their joint money. Gradually, as Jane became better at managing, it was possible to phase out this daily allowance system.

Partners may find money problems particularly worrying. If the illness prevents one or both of you from working, financial problems may indeed cause great hardship, particularly if there are young children. Sometimes it will be realistic for partners to **change roles**, so that the person with the mental illness helps in the home while the other goes out to work. Often even simple household tasks will be too much for the sick person, especially just after returning home from hospital, and other friends and relatives may have to help with child care and housework.

People sometimes fail to claim all the benefits to which they are entitled, and your relative may need your help in such matters. Some guidance is given on this in Appendix 1.

What can be done if your relative cannot manage his or her affairs because of mental illness?

If you are worried because your relative seems to be getting into difficulties in managing money or property, you may suggest that he or she takes out a **power of attorney** authorising you or another person to handle affairs. This is a legal document which a solicitor will help you with. It depends on your relative being able to understand the significance of signing the document; if he or she becomes mentally incapable afterwards, the power is revoked. Your relative may also personally revoke it at any time.

If your relative is so mentally disordered that the power of attorney would be invalid, you can apply to the **Court of Protection**, which is part of the Supreme Court and staffed by judges (the address is given in Appendix 2). The Court itself will advise you about the correct procedure: it will assess the medical evidence and may appoint a **Receiver**, who may be a court official but is usually a relative or close friend. He or she has control over the patient's property, and duties such as investing money, settling debts and keeping property in good repair. The Court can also conduct legal business for the patient, such as divorce proceedings or making a will. Unlike an ordinary power of attorney, patients cannot revoke this arrangement. They must be told of an application to the Court of Protection, and can object if they think it is unreasonable, but they must then write to the Court within seven days of being informed or before the hearing, whichever is the later. They may provide their own medical witnesses as to their fitness.

The affairs of an individual that have been taken over by the Court are examined from time to time by officers appointed by the Lord Chancellor. These **Lord Chancellor's Visitors** have the duty to see that things are being managed properly and for the patient's benefit. If you are not the receiver, and are worried that your relative's affairs are not being properly handled, consider writing yourself to the Court of Protection.

The Court does have a duty to be cautious. In our experience, this can sometimes make it a rather inflexible and bureaucratic organisation. For this reason, it is best to invoke its help only when absolutely necessary, as it may later make decisions that you cannot change and would not have wished.

Children in the family

You may worry that other members of the family, especially the sick person's children, will be adversely affected by the strain of living with someone suffering a severe mental illness. It is, of course, impossible to rule this out, particularly if the illness leads to financial or other hardships, or to upsets like having to move house or change schools frequently. However, many children, whatever their parents' mental health, have to cope with these things. Help from neighbours, friends and other relatives may be crucial in relieving strains, and will provide children with other adults to turn to if necessary. Some simple, reasonable explanation should always be given, even to younger ones. Confusing messages about 'Daddy going away', without any reason being given, can make children feel insecure and upset, or even that in some way it is their fault. It may be helpful to talk to a child, during a period of calm, about some of the experiences that the parent has when he or she is ill. Compare those experiences with being in a dream, not necessarily a pleasant one, that continues even when the parent is awake. You can use this to explain why he or she may be preoccupied or upset, or may seem less caring or less interested in the child. Older children can often be supportive, if they are given a chance to understand the problems, and if difficulties are dealt with calmly so that upsetting or frightening crises are avoided. If problems do become too difficult, families with dependent children will normally be given prompt help from professionals, such as the local social services department, child guidance clinic, or the mental health team dealing with the adult patient.

Occasionally, where there are children, family problems may seen insurmountable. In these circumstances the local authority social services department or hospital social worker may well be able to help. Their aim will always be to try to prevent the children from leaving the family home. They may be able to offer domestic help or a substitute carer who will live in while the parent is in hospital, or while the other parent is at work. In exceptional circumstances children may be temporarily received into the care of the local authority and placed with foster parents or in a children's home. This occurs only if there is no familiar alternative person, such as another relative or friend, who is able and suitable to care for them. If there are financial difficulties, the local authority can pay temporary carers.

Another worry that families have is the possibility that children may **inherit** the tendency to the disorder. This risk is real, but differs according to circumstances. The worst situation, when both parents have a severe mental illness, is very unusual. In this case, around half of the children will be affected by it. Overall, the risk that a child with one parent affected and one unaffected by schizophrenia will also develop the illness is about 10 per cent, but this varies, depending on a number of factors. The risk is smaller when schizophrenia in the parent is associated with a recognisable non-inherited cause, such as **birth injury**, or, later on, **head injury** or **epilepsy**. It is also smaller if there is no one else in the family with such problems. The risk is greater when the parent's schizophrenia is of a severe type.

Manic depressive illness, particularly the bipolar type, also runs in families. With bipolar and severe unipolar illness this is mainly because it is inherited, not because people in families tend to share troubles and difficulties that might cause depression. The inherited risk for bipolar disorder is probably about the same as for schizophrenia, that for unipolar disorder a bit smaller.

The fact that these disorders are partly inherited raises the question of whether people who develop them should choose to have children, if they haven't already done so. Most professionals would feel that the genetic risk in the majority of cases is of a degree that should not necessarily deter possible parents. Obviously, this is a decision that must be taken by each couple. And the genetic risk is only one consideration—more important is whether the illness seriously undermines the individual's ability to carry out the duties and everyday responsibilities of parenthood.

Finally, there is no reason why the unaffected brothers and sisters of a person with one of these conditions should not themselves have children: here the genetic risk is very small indeed.

In some health centres, it is possible to get advice on these matters from a special **genetic counselling service**. It may be worth asking if there is one in your area.

Relapse

In most cases, particularly if relapse has occurred before, you will be the best judge of whether your relative is becoming ill again. However, some pointers may be useful, as these illnesses often do follow a relapsing course whose development may not closely resemble the original form of the illness.

Relapses are recognised by changes in behaviour. One of the problems in spotting the early stages of relapse is that these changes often happen gradually. This means that it may be very difficult to distinguish between normal behaviour and that due to the recurrence of the illness.

For example, one of the changes that occur in **mania** is increased **irritability**. If your mentally ill relative loses his or her temper, it is often hard to tell if this is a normal response, or a bit excessive for this particular person in these particular circumstances. This is the sort of judgement you are liable to be extremely good at, as you live with the person all the time.

Unfortunately, one of the common complaints that are levelled at clinical staff is that they do not believe that carers can pick up such subtle changes, and so do not act upon the information, thus failing to prevent a crisis from developing.

What symptoms should you look out for? In **schizophrenia**, small changes in someone's normal pattern can give a clue. Sufferers may stay up into the small hours, sometimes compensating by rising at a later time. They may go off their food, or eat in a more faddy way. They may spend increasing amounts of time on their own, shying away from the company of the family or of visitors. They may not look after themselves so well and may behave in awkward or obstinate ways. They may be increasingly suspicious and wary. They may smile less and become more distant. A chance remark may suggest that they are returning to the preoccupations they had when they were ill. One wife knew that her husband was relapsing when he lost interest in going to the day centre, spent more and more time in bed, and began talking again of 'the aliens' in the TV programmes that he watched. In many people with schizophrenia, relapse is heralded by the feelings of tenseness and nervousness that we all experience from time to time, but which in them may mean something more sinister.

The major changes may be of **mood**: an individual may be increasingly nervous or depressed. However, people with schizophrenia sometimes become depressed without it indicating relapse: they may have enough to be depressed about, and it can be hard to distinguish the reactions to an unrewarding situation from the symptoms of relapse.

Relapse in **unipolar depression** is often gradual. Individuals slowly become less energetic, doing less about the house. They lose pleasure in things that they usually enjoy. They become quieter and less sociable. They may have trouble getting off to sleep, or wake much too early in the morning. They take less pleasure in eating and may eat less, leaving food on the plate. They may surprise you by bursting into tears in response to what seemed a fairly harmless remark.

In contrast, the return of **mania** may be suggested by an increased energy. The individual becomes noticeably more jovial, and may start to make plans or start organising things. One woman's husband knew she was relapsing when she took over the task of walking the dog and began to make slightly unrealistic plans for a return to work. Alteration in sleep patterns are often a clear early sign—typically, people suddenly need less sleep. Your relative may begin to stay up late and be more talkative than usual. He or she may eat more and hurry over a meal, and may also become more irritable.

If you do think your relative is relapsing, you must try to take action (some guidance is given on p. 46).

All the changes described above can be seen in a fully fledged relapse. In the early stages, they are much less pronounced—which can be a real problem for you. On the one hand, if you can recognise a relapse early, it can be nipped in the bud by prompt treatment. On the other, the relationship may become more difficult if you are always on the alert for signs of relapse, and if everything your relative does is evaluated in order to discern whether it is normal or whether it might be the effect of illness. Obviously, a balance has to be struck—a balance that you will have to reach in the light of your own particular experiences, and perhaps by discussing it beforehand with your relative.

It is also possible that if he or she starts refusing to take medication, a relapse will become more likely over the next few months. This is a problem looked at in more detail when we discuss treatments in Chapter 5.

3 Community Care in the 1990s

Community care started nearly fifty years ago. In fact, the number of in-patients in mental hospitals in the UK peaked in 1954, so that, ever since, there have been increasing numbers of people living in the community who previously were, or would have been, in mental hospitals. Some of these are able to live at home because of innovative programmes of rehabilitation and accommodation. However, in many cases, it has just meant placing additional burdens on relatives. The process of reducing hospital beds, for psychiatric patients as well as for medical, accelerated in the 1980s. Unhappily, the services developed to deal with community care for people with severe mental illness have always lagged behind what has been needed. Services have very rarely been coordinated to work efficiently for the benefit of clients.

Policy changes since 1985

There was a very critical report of the Parliamentary Select Committee on Health and Social Services in 1985, and as a result the government developed a more detailed policy designed to integrate care both across the various services and over time. These initiatives are important for clients and carers alike, not least because they all recognise the rights of both groups to be consulted and involved in planning care services. Obviously, the fact that the government of the day issues a directive does not necessarily mean that the directive will be put into practice. However, it is worth knowing about these directives because they can be used to pressure the local psychiatric services into making provision for you and your relative if they appear reluctant or incapable of doing so.

Not all the policy changes since this time have been clearly beneficial. One of the initiatives, which followed the 1988

Griffiths Report on community care, involved separating social and medical care. While this was perhaps not inappropriate in the care of the elderly, in our view it has made it very difficult to provide services for people with severe mental disorder, for the simple reason that the social difficulties that they face are very closely tied in with their mental health problems. Under this initiative, local authority social services were given the lead in providing social care. In consequence, the funding and responsibilities of the mental health services were considerably curtailed by the 1990 National Health Service and Community Care Act. The effect of this split between social and medical care has been a considerable duplication of effort—which is reflected in the two parallel systems for providing care, the **care management** operated by local authority social services, and the **Care Programme Approach (CPA)** of the mental health services. If you look at what is involved in these systems, it becomes clear how similar they are. This has been tacitly recognised by the government, with the issuing of various guidelines for integrating the two approaches. The latest production in a series of documents, called *Building Bridges*, was published in 1996. This is a guide to arrangements for inter-agency working for the care and protection of severely mentally ill people.

One of the great advances in government policy on community care has been the absolute recognition that **services should be proportional to the need**. In other words, people with the greatest needs should have access to the most resources. But there has been one major disadvantage to the new system. When such people were cared for in old-style psychiatric hospitals, all the facilities and services available to them were under one roof. When care was shifted to the community, however, this was no longer the case: clients were faced with a set of services usually in different places and managed by different agencies. This arrangement would tax most people, but is especially problematical for users of mental health services and their carers. It is difficult enough for professionals to find their way around such a network of services, so it is not surprising that clients sometimes don't get the services they need, even though they may exist. Occasionally these inefficiencies in the system can cause things to go badly wrong.

The Care Programme Approach

It was for this reason that the **Care Programme Approach** was brought in. This obliges people responsible for the care of somebody with a serious mental health problem to consider exactly what his or her needs are (by means of a **needs assessment**). Serious thought is then given to how the various needs might be met, given the available services and facilities—this is the **care plan**. Clearly, it will be of little use unless it is put into practice, and in order to make sure this happens the progress of clients is monitored and regularly reviewed. It is accepted as essential to the Care Programme Approach that both clients themselves and their carers should be involved as much as possible in the planning.

The idea of **continuity of care** is an essential plank in this style of working. It is pretty obvious stuff, really. The idea is that if you are looked after by somebody who knows you as a person, and has done so over a period of time, then he or she is likely to be much more attuned to your needs and readier to respond when things go wrong, as they sometimes do.

The Care Programme Approach was introduced in 1991 to provide a framework for the care of mentally ill people outside hospitals. The district health authorities and local authority social services departments are expected to collaborate in setting up arrangements for the care and treatment of mentally ill people in the community. In addition to the aspects of the Care Programme Approach described above, another central feature is the appointment of **key workers** to keep in close touch with the client and carer and to make sure that the programme is going well. Key workers have many responsibilities. They have to organise all aspects of care, even though they may not carry them out themselves. They have to form the main therapeutic relationship with their clients and they must ensure that clients both get and accept the treatment they need. They act as a channel of communication between the client and carer and the community mental health team. They also liaise with outside agencies, particularly social services departments. Finally, they act as advocate, adviser and friend to their clients.

Another thing that the Care Programme Approach does is to make official, as it were, the idea of team working. Multidisciplinary teams have existed here and there for fifteen or twenty years, and are an effective way of using the variety of knowledge and expertise of the different professional groups: nurses, doctors, psychologists, occupational therapists, social workers. But while a number of psychiatric teams were truly multidisciplinary, the term was actually used to cover a whole range of working styles. Sometimes they reflected rivalries between the different professional groups, rather than the mutual respect which is indispensable for working together.

The CPA affords very powerful official recognition to the idea that carers should be involved in a big way in planning treatment and services for their sick relatives. The CPA guidelines say that carers' contributions to meeting clients' needs should be explicitly recognised in the care plan. Help from the mental health services should include meeting carers' needs for support, periods of respite care, and twenty-four-hour access to an emergency mental health service. It must be said that these represent aspirations rather than realities, but at least the health and social services can be held to account for not providing them.

Since it is the government's intention that the social and medical assessments involved in working up a care programme should not be done separately, good liaison between social services departments and community mental health teams is essential. However, in practice, social services departments, at least in inner-city areas like the ones where we work, are so hopelessly overstretched that sometimes care programmes and assessments are made without the presence of social workers. While this is to be deplored, there does not seem a ready way around it as long as local authority social service budgets are so constrained.

Some of the requirements for providing care for clients with severe mental health problems are embodied in law. Thus, Section 117 of the Mental Health Act 1983 requires health authorities and local authorities to provide after-care for people who have been detained in hospital under certain Sections of the Mental Health Act. This is essentially Section 3, together with some of the Sections which allow court orders to be made for patients who have committed offences. In fact, the Care Programme Approach supersedes what used to be called the Section 117 requirement. What it means basically is that everyone who is in need of the specialist mental health services should have a care programme assessment.

Finally, if a client is assessed as needing to be on a care programme because of ongoing severe mental health problems or vulnerability, the mental health team will allocate a key worker with responsibility to plan and organise services for him or her, in consultation with both client and carer. The care plan must be formally reviewed at least every six months by the mental health team. If you live with someone with a severe mental health problem it is a good idea for you to make sure that he or she has had a care programme assessment. If not, you should ask the GP to refer your relative to your local mental health team so that they can carry one out.

The purchaser/provider split and the role of the GP

Another of the recent changes that have occurred in the Health Service has been the splitting of the district health authorities into separate bodies: the **purchaser/provider split**. District health authorities are now essentially agents for buying health care. They do so from 'provider services', which are now almost invariably **NHS Trusts**. This has the interesting effect of keeping the Trusts on their toes in the matter of providing the services they are paid for. Purchasers must now ensure that their contracts with providers actually set out that the Care Programme Approach is fully implemented and that **Supervision Registers** (see p. 72) are maintained. This is therefore a local method of ensuring high-quality services.

It has also been increasingly recognised that the housing needs of people with severe mental illness can be quite complicated. In order to meet these needs, there has to be a range of housing with different levels of support. Although housing is a form of social provision, when people being housed have mental illness it is obviously of interest to health care providers too. For this reason, health authorities (purchasers) are encouraged to work together with local authorities to ensure that there is a proper supply of housing specially for people with mental health problems. They can even do this by joining together (**joint commissioning**) with the local authority to fund the housing projects necessary. The effect of all this is that there is still a deficiency in the right sort of housing in many areas, but at least pressure is being brought to bear to change matters.

Family doctors are now the most important link between

families and the specialist services. People running specialist services are now encouraged to involve family doctors in care planning and to ensure, at any rate, that they know who clients' key workers are, and how to get hold of services in an emergency, particularly out of hours. Recently, the Department of Health has given GPs the power to remove violent patients from their lists immediately. However, if the violence may have arisen because of mental illness, the needs of the patient must be dealt with before considering removal from the GP's list. Occasionally people with severe mental illness do get involved in incidents at GPs' surgeries. It is useful to know that if this makes it impossible for the GP to continue caring for the patient, the GP must, at any rate, arrange for alternative services to meet the patient's needs. It is regarded as good practice for family doctors who feel they must remove someone from their list to inform the community mental health team before they do so.

The specialist psychiatric services

The specialist psychiatric services have been given a number of principles to follow when providing services for mentally ill people. Apart from those we have already mentioned, they are encouraged to respect the individual qualities and social, cultural, linguistic and religious background of their clients. As well as taking into account the needs, wishes and convenience both of clients and of their carers, services are encouraged to give people as much self-determination as possible. This means that in principle clients should be able, for instance, to choose the gender of their health or social care-worker.

An increasing amount of attention is being paid to the role of voluntary organisations in the overall provision of services for people with mental health problems. The report of the inquiry into the care and treatment of Christopher Clunis (mentioned on p. 27) recommended that a system of 'befrienders' should be set up. Such befrienders would be specially recruited and trained to work with mentally ill people.

Another area where there has been a great deal of development in the last ten years or so has been in the contribution of private providers of services and care. What usually happens here is that the health care purchaser contracts with a private provider—for instance, to provide supportive accommodation. This arrangement is potentially dangerous if the providers do not have appropriate or adequate experience or resources. Indeed, it will only work well if the private services are monitored, to make sure that they observe the established procedures for working with people with mental health problems and follow government policy for mental health services. This includes, for example, using the Care Programme Approach and maintaining confidentiality in the proper way. They must also liaise closely with the local specialist mental health services. The health care purchasers have an obligation to make sure that good practices are observed in the private sector.

If your relative is receiving care and treatment in some kind of private setting, and you think that things are going wrong, complain first of all to the mental health team, and secondly to the district health authority.

Mental health clients and the courts

Unfortunately, one of the things that sometimes happens when people with severe mental health problems are living at home is that they come into contact with the courts. This may be because of some kind of public incident, not necessarily a violent one—a whole range of petty crimes are occasionally committed by people who are mentally disordered. If they are arrested as a result, they are quite likely to end up appearing in court. In the past this has sometimes meant that people were sentenced without proper regard to their mental health needs. Again, the government has recently been issuing guidance to people working in the criminal justice system on how to work with colleagues in the health care sector. Even so, there are all too many occasions when the psychiatric needs of people with severe mental illness are not properly considered when they appear in the courts. In such circumstances, you may have to be the first supporter of your relative. This may involve pestering lawyers and court officials to make sure they know about the mental health problem.

Involving relatives and friends

As already mentioned, one of the important developments in the attitude of the government and its agents has been the acceptance that 'users'' (clients') relatives and other carers should be involved as far as possible in the organisation of care. Carers are seen as having a particular role in helping mental health teams to identify the needs of clients, in helping them to keep in touch with clients, and in encouraging clients to keep to their care plans. Indeed, the principle is that, provided the client agrees, carers should receive a copy of the care plan.

The idea of involving the relatives and friends of people with health problems is one of the expectations set out in the Patients' Charter. The Department of Health published a framework for local community care charters early in 1996, the key part of which is putting clients and carers first. The idea is that local agencies will be committed to involving clients and carers in the assessment process and in care planning. They must respect clients' personal beliefs, show courtesy and respect at all times, and set a high standard in dealing with letters and inquiries. They must also act to protect the confidentiality of information.

Problems sometimes arise if the client refuses to have his or her relatives involved. Members of the mental health team should then try to persuade the client of the benefit of such contact. If, however, he or she remains adamant that family, or carers, should not be involved, the mental health services are obliged to respect these wishes. There are some exceptions. One is where, for example, approved social workers (see p. 77) are required by law to inform the nearest relative if someone is being considered for compulsory detention, or has already been detained. Another is where public interest outweighs the imperative of confidentiality. This might arise, for instance, if the client was making specific threats which involved the carer.

The protection of information

This brings us to another important set of guidelines—those concerned with the protection of information generally. As might be imagined, there are conflicting requirements. On the one hand, where a number of mental health professionals and social services professionals work together for the good of a client, they need to have the fullest possible information so that their judgements and decisions can be the best possible. When people with severe mental health disorders are difficult to help, the failure to communicate may lead to real problems, and sometimes tragedies, as in the case of Christopher Clunis. On the other hand, the government recognises that people with such problems are entitled to the same confidential handling of information as any other health or social services client.

Information about clients is protected in a number of ways. First, mental health professionals follow codes of conduct placing very strict limits on the disclosure of information, and this is backed up by their professional disciplinary organisation. So, for example, a doctor can be severely disciplined by the General Medical Council if he or she breaches patient confidentiality. In addition, information about clients is covered by a well established common law 'duty of confidence'. Finally, if the information is held on a computer, it is specifically protected by the Data Protection Act of 1984. The government have also recently adopted a European Union directive on data protection. One general rule is that information given for one purpose may not be given to a third party, or used for a different purpose, without the consent of clients. But this is not a rigid rule, because it might sometimes act to the detriment of clients.

Clients and carers should know that personal information may need to pass between health service personnel, local authority services and people working for other agencies such as probation and housing, and the voluntary sector. Usually this is part of the normal care planning process, and unless clients object information is given on a need-to-know basis to people with a direct interest—and somebody given information in this way should not pass it on to a third party unless that person is entitled to it. People with a direct interest could include, for instance, somebody employed by a private nursing home. If clients or carers object to this passage of information, it may mean that the whole process of planning care has to be reorganised. Occasionally information may be passed on without the client's consent—where a history of violence, for example, necessitates that this be done in the public interest. And occasionally clinical workers may need to take legal advice as to whether it is permissible to pass on confidential information.

Clients, or somebody authorised to act on their behalf, have the statutory right to know what information is on record about them. Access to computerised records is primarily given by the Data Protection Act of 1984; clients cannot be prevented from having access to such records, even if it may involve the risk of serious harm to another individual. Clients also have the right of access to written records under the Access to Health Records Act 1990; this applies only to records that were made on or after 1 November 1991. Even then, there are circumstances under which clients may not be entitled to see their records. For instance, if the record holder thinks that it would cause serious harm to the physical or mental health of the client, or to anyone else, they can withhold access; and they can do so where the records contain information which relates to, or is provided by, some non-professional person, if that person can be identified and has not consented to its disclosure. Although clients don't actually have a right to see any of their records preceding 1991, the record holder may allow them access. Basically, the guiding principle is that clients should be allowed to know what is written about then whenever possible.

Your local psychiatric services are obliged to have a written policy on access to records, which you can ask them for. Usually this would state that if the client makes a request to see his or her records, this should happen within twenty-one days from the date of application. Clients can also authorise other people to seek access to health information about them. Obviously, under these circumstances, the staff must make absolutely sure that such persons really are acting at the request of the client.

Supervision Registers

You may have heard about **Supervision Registers**. Various local services have operated 'at risk' registers for some time. Then, in response to concerns that community care was not working as well as it should for the most severely mentally ill people, the Department of Health introduced Supervision Registers nationally from 1 April 1994. The intention behind these registers is to identify people with a severe mental illness that makes them a significant risk to themselves or (particularly) to others, in order to ensure that local psychiatric services focus effectively on them. In general, people can be put on the Supervision Register if they are liable to be at significant risk of committing serious violence or suicide, or if they are in danger because they are likely to seriously neglect themselves. The decision as to whether or not to include somebody on the Supervision Register is usually made in the normal discussion of the care programme before he or she leaves hospital, although sometimes it is made later on. The ultimate responsibility for it is borne by the consultant psychiatrist in charge of the client's care (the Responsible Medical Officer, or RMO). However, the consultant psychiatrist must consult widely before doing so. The fact that a client is on the Supervision Register means that somebody thinks there may be problems in the future. Most authorities include their Supervision Register within a wider Care Programme Register to avoid duplication.

The idea of the Supervision Register is not to change the way that people are cared for, or to stigmatise them, but to ensure that what has been planned actually happens. In particular, it is important that people at this level of risk don't drop out of the care system. Clients should be informed of a decision to place them on the Supervision Register, but just occasionally teams may decide not to tell a client that he or she is on it. But this should happen only in exceptional circumstances, and only temporarily.

The ordinary rules of confidentiality are strictly applied to the information held on the Care Programme Register or the Supervision Register. Again, this information is released on a need-to-know basis. In fact, in most cases the actual register records will not be available to external agencies, although selected information from them may be passed on. In normal circumstances, the specific information that an individual is on the Supervision Register would not be given to the general public.

The decision to put somebody on the register has to be constantly reviewed. If he or she moves from one area to another, the original mental health team have an obligation to liaise with the new one. Usually, this will involve the inclusion of the client on the Supervision Register of the new area.

For someone who thinks he or she ought not to be on the Supervision Register, there is no specific way of appealing. So, for example, there is no right of appeal to a Mental Health Review Tribunal, since the Supervision Register doesn't imply any form of detention. If you, or your relative, feel that the register is being used inappropriately, you have the usual right of appeal for a second opinion, or you can use the local complaint procedures.

4 Services

The people involved in the care of your relative

As described in Chapter 3, mental health services are currently organised in **multidisciplinary teams**. Nowadays these are likely to include a **team leader**, who will usually be a senior nurse, plus a **consultant psychiatrist** and a variety of other members. You may meet some from other disciplines, such as occupational therapy, community nursing, clinical psychology and social work, as the team will designate two or three people who will become involved in the care of your relative. One of these will be the **key worker** (see p. 65). A key worker may be from any discipline—a community psychiatric nurse (CPN), a social worker, an occupational therapist, a senior house officer or a clinical psychologist—depending on your relative's particular problems, so it may sometimes seem as though 'the doctor' never sees him or her.

The team meet regularly to discuss the progress of each client, and if your relative is being cared for under the Care Programme Approach he or she has by law to be discussed (reviewed) at least every six months. Clients sometimes feel that, although they have been 'under Doctor Smith', they have been seen only once or twice by him, so he cannot have known much about them. But if the team is working properly this will not be the case, because each member will keep the others informed. The main advantage of this team approach is that the client is seen as a whole person, who may have needs that are best satisfied by a particular member of the team, not necessarily the psychiatrist. It also means that you do not have to rely just on one member of staff, who may be unavailable or with whom you may have disagreements. The disadvantage is that you may feel you never get to talk to the same person, and sometimes none of them may seem to know what is happening! This can be a real problem, particularly in a crisis, but a good team will try not to let it happen often.

Although many people do not realise this, **psychiatrists** have to train as ordinary medical doctors first, which takes five or six years. In this country, they then have to undertake a further six years or so of training in psychiatry. After about three years of this training, they will sit the entrance examination for membership of the **Royal College of Psychiatrists**. If they pass, they are entitled to put 'MRCPsych' after their names—initials you may have seen, for instance, in correspondence. After a further period of supervised work, they may apply for posts as consultants.

Clearly, this is a long training; sad to say, even these days clients and their relatives sometimes feel it must have failed to achieve its aim, producing as end result a psychiatrist who may not appear very good at offering support and information.

Consultants are assisted by more junior doctors who are part of the way through their training. In the past these were **senior registrars**, **registrars** and **house officers**. Senior registrars were also usually members of the Royal College of Psychiatry. Recently, the categorisation of these doctors in training has changed, so that there is now a general junior doctor category of 'senior house officer' and a category for psychiatrists in specialist training who have taken the membership exam, who are called 'specialist grade registrars'.

One popular image of psychiatrists, perhaps the most common one, is of a very powerful individual who behaves rather oddly and has an uncanny ability to see into the deep recesses of the mind. The truth is more down-to-earth. A good psychiatrist may have insights into a situation that you may not have thought of, but this comes from long experience and an objective alertness to all the possibilities. Psychiatrists need information to do this, and this is why assessment involves so many questions (see p. 81). They may be better at detecting false information than untrained people, but they are still far from infallible. One of us (Paul) is a consultant psychiatrist:

> I work with two teams. One is located on a general psychiatric ward, and includes psychiatric nurses of different grades, an occupational therapist and a senior house officer. The beds on the ward are always full—indeed, in our unit

bed occupation is said to run at over 110 per cent. This does not mean that people share beds(!), but that the beds of people who are on leave from the ward or beds in the private sector are used to cope with the overflow of patients. The second team is a community mental health team. This has a base outside the hospital, and consists of community psychiatric nurses and an occupational therapist. The two teams share a specialist grade registrar and a clinical psychologist. Between them they are responsible for an area of inner London with a population of thirty-eight thousand.

As I am primarily an academic psychiatrist, and also have quite a lot of managerial responsibilities, I job-share this National Health Service work with a colleague. Currently, two of my sessions are team meetings on the ward. People with fairly severe episodes of mental disorder are admitted to the ward, where they are assessed by the various team members. In the team meeting I hear about these new patients and see them, and the team comes to conclusions about diagnosis, treatment and management that will best help them. In this I operate a bit like the chairman of a committee, summing up the consensus view of my colleagues. For some purposes, as Responsible Medical Officer I am supposed to have the final word, but decisions are almost always by joint agreement.

I also hear about the progress of patients admitted earlier, but do not have time to see more than a few of them each week. However, I do see them at Care Programme Approach meetings, which is when important decisions are made—for instance, about discharge arrangements or applications for supported accommodation. Sometimes I see the patients' relatives, although this is also done by other members of the team. Some of my time is used to teach and supervise my junior colleagues, who are responsible for the everyday medical input in the ward, and I also do some out-patient and community work. This is an efficient way of using limited resources. It is a common pattern of working, repeated in wards and clinics throughout Britain. Some consultants also run out-patient clinics in general practice health centres, a trend that is increasing.

Nurses, too, are organised into various grades. The head nurse in a ward is sometimes called the **ward manager**. After a psychiatric training lasting three years, nurses become **Registered Mental Nurses** (RMNs). Some mental health nurses are also **State Registered Nurses** (SRNs)—that is, they have a general nursing qualification; and some, particularly these days, have taken degrees in nursing or related subjects.

Many mental health nurses work in hospital wards and clinics. Increasingly, however, nurses spend most of their time visiting patients in their homes—these are the **community psychiatric nurses** (CPNs). They have all had long experience of psychiatric nursing, often as ward managers. They will also have undertaken training courses in community psychiatry. Such nurses usually have their base in a community mental health centre, but a few work directly with family doctors. They are mainly closely involved in the treatment of people who have been discharged from hospital following serious episodes of mental illness. They keep an eye on patients' medication, and may give injections. They monitor the general situation of the patients and their families, and provide a significant source of advice and support. They also keep the other members of the community mental health team informed of progress, so they form an important channel of communication.

Neil has been a community psychiatric nurse for about three years. During most of this time he has been visiting Phil, a young man of about his own age who suffers from schizophrenia. Phil has been reasonably well, and able to live at home with his parents. There are rarely any problems, but sometimes Phil's parents like to be able to talk things over with Neil, which he is always ready to do. Indeed, he has become something of a friend to all the family. He also gives Phil a long-lasting injection every three weeks. Recently Phil began to experience a return of some disturbing symptoms, but with Neil's help he and his family were able to cope with this and things settled down again. The enduring relationship that has developed between Neil and Phil and his family is a good example of the valuable role of many community psychiatric nurses in helping people manage the problems of a serious mental illness.

Social workers play a considerable role in psychiatry. They may be involved with individual patients, offering **support** and

counselling, and using a range of techniques aimed at improving the patient's ability to cope. They also have **expert knowledge** about welfare rights, practical aids and community facilities. They have particular powers and duties under the **Mental Health Act** and the Community Care Acts to provide needs assessments. Social workers are normally based in local authority offices, and have links with mental health teams. In inner-city areas like the ones we work in, local authority social services are even more stretched than the mental health teams.

Social workers who carry out functions under the Mental Health Act must have additional training and be approved by a local authority—they are known as ASWs (approved social workers). Each local authority is required to have its training programme authorised by the Central Council for Education and Training in Social Work. Like CPNs, social workers often provide help and support for many mentally ill people and their families over a long period. Many social workers have a particular interest in the difficulties that families experience, and may spend a lot of time visiting patients' homes. They should have a knowledge of what is available in the community to help the mentally ill.

Social workers frequently get a bad press, but they are often unfairly, and sometimes unconsciously, blamed for the very problems they are trying to help with. Some of these problems are unlikely to go away, and the aim of the social worker may be merely to make them a bit more bearable. He or she is then blamed for failing to do the impossible and accused of 'doing nothing'. Clearly, as with any other profession, not all social workers are equally effective. Nevertheless, most give excellent and determined support to people with great and enduring difficulties.

Clinical psychologists have a degree in psychology, following which they undergo a further three-year specialist clinical training. This training now leads to a doctorate in clinical psychology. Some have also taken another research-based degree (a PhD). Both of these routes mean that they are called 'Doctor'. You may perhaps have been confused by this use of the term, not being sure if the person you are talking to is a doctor of the medical sort or has a different expertise.

Clinical psychologists specialise in **assessing** and **treating** psychological problems of all kinds. They also have an interest in **measuring** and **evaluating** people's progress. Clinical psychology is still a relatively small profession. Its members are normally based in mental health teams, working in community health centres, with GPs, or in general hospitals. One of us, Elizabeth, is a consultant clinical psychologist:

> I work with a multidisciplinary team which sees all those in the local area who have adult mental health problems, but is particularly geared to helping those with severe mental illness. Members of our team are all linked with our local GP practices, and clients are seen at the GP practice, in their homes, at a local drop-in centre or at our team base, a house in the local community. We have beds in a local ward for those who require admission—these are always full. We receive referrals mainly from GPs but also from social services, and from other teams telling us that someone has moved into our area and that we need to take over their care.
>
> As I work in a deprived inner-London area, with a variety of ethnic minority clients, the problems we have to deal with can be very diverse and sometimes alarming: a client may have been attacked, or evicted and so need help with housing; others need help from the social services or physical health agencies on account of a multitude of overlapping difficulties. I key-work around ten clients, and have a particular interest in those with long-term psychosis.
>
> Psychologists are specialists in cognitive behavioural treatments, which means that we talk to people about both what they think (cognition) and what they do (behaviour), and we try to help them change negative thought patterns or unhelpful behaviour patterns that can make anxiety, depression or psychosis more problematic. Psychologists offer such 'talking therapies' to individuals, carers and groups, discuss the particular psychological problems of other key workers' clients, and help the team review care plans for everyone on its case load. Psychologists do not prescribe drug treatments—this is the responsibility of the psychiatrists in the teams.
>
> I have a research interest in offering help to relatives who look after a mentally ill family member, and see families

at home. I have also run relatives' groups. I encourage other staff to be supportive of carers, and advise them of the best ways of doing this. More recently, I have developed with colleagues new ways of discussing the experience of psychosis with clients, and of trying to help them understand and cope with it more effectively. These new approaches, individual 'talking therapies', seem to be effective, and are increasingly likely to be available in the future from your local mental health team.

In medicine as a whole, there are a number of **remedial** professions, which include physiotherapy and speech therapy. Within psychiatry, **occupational therapy** is by far the most prominent of these. Occupational therapists undergo a three-year training course. Their job is to design and carry out programmes of activities intended to **overcome disability** and to foster or maintain **personal functioning**. These programmes may be based in the hospital ward, in the occupational therapy department, or in the community, where some occupational therapists are now based, doing key work with the rest of the team. The work of the occupational therapist is described in more detail on pp. 116–17.

There is, in practice, a lot of overlap in what members of these professions do when they see clients. Much of the assessment and treatment of psychiatric disorders is carried out during the process of getting to know patients and by talking to them over a considerable period of time. Each profession has its own particular specialist knowledge as well, and psychiatric services are usually organised in teams because this is an efficient way of using the different contributions that each profession can make. A good team should be of great assistance to you and your relative. Occasionally, though, there are disadvantages to the team set-up. If the team is badly organised, there may be failures of communication: for instance, each team member may think that someone else is dealing with a particular problem, when in fact no one is. If there is a possibility that this has happened in your relative's case, raise the matter with your key worker or the person on the team that you have had most contact with.

The services available to your relative
For most people who become mentally ill, the professional they see first is the **general practitioner (GP)**, otherwise known as the family practitioner or family doctor. They will usually be seen, by appointment or on spec, in the GP's surgery, although if a surgery appointment isn't feasible GPs will sometimes make a home visit. They normally deal with minor cases themselves, but will **refer** more serious conditions to the psychiatric team. This is commonly done by making an out-patient appointment for your relative to see a psychiatrist. This will often take place at your local general or psychiatric hospital, although many psychiatrists have sessions in community resource centres, and a few in health centres.

If an appointment *is* made for your mentally ill relative, you should be aware that there is likely to be some delay—a few weeks, perhaps—before he or she is seen. Psychiatrists like their patients to be accompanied to appointments, partly so that they have a further source of information on tap if they need it. Don't be reticent about asking to see the psychiatrist if he or she does not suggest it, or about seeking answers to your queries. Your relative may have to wait for some time at the hospital or centre, particularly if he or she is seen first by the registrar, who will then discuss things with the consultant. Going with relatives to the appointment will give them some company while they wait—this may be especially appreciated if they are feeling apprehensive about it. Another route to the psychiatric team is to be seen first by any of its members, who will do an initial assessment and then discuss with the rest of the team what services the individual needs.

Sometimes more urgent action seems necessary, and the GP will arrange for a **home visit** by the psychiatrist or another member of the multidisciplinary team, who will come to your home and assess your relative there. This can be arranged within a day or two.

Psychiatric professionals **assess** patients largely by collecting information, both from the ill people themselves and from their relatives, and even occasionally from other acquaintances. They do this in order to discover what form the illness takes, what sort of person the sufferer normally is, and what stresses and strains he or she has been exposed to. The psychiatrist will usually obtain information about your relative's symptoms directly from him or her, but may back this up by getting an account from you or other members of the family. A client's relatives will often be the best people to describe the way the illness has developed. In addition, the psychiatrist will gather background information that provides the overall context within which to understand the origins of the disorder. This means that he may well receive information from your family doctor, and from local authority social workers if they have been involved.

Nowadays, in many areas, assessments are carried out by members of a community mental health team, at a community resource centre of some kind, or by visiting your relative at home. Obviously, it is very important that the information you give to members of the mental health team is accurate and as full as possible. Sometimes, you may feel that a question is irrelevant or intrusive, and that you would prefer not to answer it fully. But do bear in mind that covering things up may hinder the clinical staff from helping your relative.

Very occasionally, schizophrenia or manic depressive illness can be mimicked by bodily diseases. So the psychiatrist may order blood tests, and occasionally other investigations such as a brain scan, to exclude these—either as routine or because of symptoms that suggest they are appropriate.

After the client has been assessed, and if his or her condition is considered minor, the GP will often carry on the treatment. More serious problems may involve regular monitoring, and sometimes a client will need to be admitted to hospital.

Psychiatric wards are now normally based in **district general hospitals**, which are sited close to the communities they serve. Many of them were purpose-built in the 1970s, but are beginning to show their age. They sometimes have a more institutional look than we would prefer these days. In some cases they may take the form of an awkwardly placed ward or even a hospital block originally built for some other purpose and later adapted. A few areas still have their admission wards in old-style **mental hospitals**, although most of these have now closed. Many of them were built in Victorian times and served large areas, and so they may be quite a long way from your home and difficult to get to.

Finally, these days, if there are no beds in your local hospital your relative may be sent for a few days into private care; this is usually in the same city, but very occasionally a whole area will have no beds and your relative may be placed further away. (Recently a patient from London was admitted to a hospital in Leicester, but such extremes are unusual.) Usually this will be only for a few days: local services try not to use private beds for too long because they have to be paid for by the NHS and can cost £300 a night.

Most old-style long-stay wards have now closed down, and under the current guidelines and legislation relating to community care people who need continuing twenty-four-hour care are given a **needs assessment** (see page 65) by the social work department and then placed in a 'high support' hostel in the local area. They no longer stay in hospital for months or years, as they used to. A small minority of patients may be so disturbed for so long that they need to live in a secure unit, but even for them the arrangement will rarely be permanent.

In psychiatric wards, unlike most medical wards, people wear their own day clothes and night clothes, so if your relative is being admitted he or she will need to take these along, or you will have to bring them later. The new patient will be received into the ward by the nursing staff, who will register him or her by taking some personal details. Usually, after your relative has settled into the ward—perhaps an hour or two later—a junior psychiatrist will come to make a physical examination, record your relative's mental condition and set in motion some basic physical investigations. Temporary medication may be provided, to calm your relative down or to help him or her sleep. Each client has a 'named nurse', who has special responsibility for him or her and coordinates most aspects of his or her care.

Most wards these days are for both sexes. Sleeping accommodation is usually either in single rooms, or in rooms shared by from two to six patients. Most hospitals do have one ward that is kept locked, but this is reserved for the most difficult patients—for instance, those who are felt likely to commit suicide or to abscond while seriously ill. A few hospitals have special mother-and-baby units for those with post-natal psychosis; this permits a mentally ill mother to take some part in caring for her baby at this important time.

After a few days, your relative's case will be considered in a **team or management meeting**, still sometimes called a **ward round**, although this is a term borrowed from hospitals that treat physical illnesses. The consultant psychiatrist usually presides over this, and there are often quite a number of people there, representing the various clinical professions. This can be upsetting for your relative, and may be equally embarrassing for you if you have been invited along. Do remember, though, that the staff in these meetings are bound by rules of confidentiality and are there to provide a service for you and your relative. Sometimes, if a client is likely to be very upset by being seen in the team meeting, a few members of the team may come out to see him or her more privately.

Most clients admitted from their homes to psychiatric wards will return home when they are discharged. Ideally, discharge should be planned to take place in a gradual manner: it may be suggested at first that your relative returns home perhaps for an afternoon. He or she may then spend part or all of a weekend at home, and if this seems to go all right may be discharged. This pattern can be varied to suit the needs of individuals and their relatives, although most admissions to hospital are so short these days that it is not usually possible to be as flexible as one would wish. During this process it is important that you keep the clinical staff informed about how things have gone, and what you think the next step should be.

Under the new **Community Care Acts**, a patient with severe mental illness cannot be discharged from hospital without a proper discharge plan signed by the consultant and a social worker, and agreed by a carer if there is one. The discharge planning meeting (still sometimes called a 'Section 117 meeting', after the part of the Mental Health Act that describes it) is now a legal requirement, and you should be both consulted and present at it. This is so that you know of and agree with any discharge plans that are made with the team about your relative's future care, once he or she leaves hospital.

Sometimes, supported accommodation may seem a better option than going home. There are a number of possibilities, including **supervised high-support hostels** and **low-support hostels**, and **flats**, **group homes** and **supervised lodgings**.

Hostels, which may be established either by the statutory authorities or by charitable organisations, provide for a number of patients. They vary enormously: some are just places to eat and sleep, while others offer much more in the way of supervision.

Some provide long-term accommodation, whereas others are seen very much as staging-posts on the way to a full return to life in the community. In some, supervision is quite intensive, with night staff, organised daytime activities and another set of key workers. Although it may not always be feasible, the aim is to place people in the facility that best suits their level of disability.

Group homes are usually set up in large converted houses, with perhaps from four to twenty patients living in them. After the settling-in period, they are not heavily supervised, although various members of the mental health team may pop in from time to time. In most ways they are just like an ordinary home: the residents have their own rooms, but share other facilities. They have to work out amongst themselves who does what in the important matters of cooking and cleaning. Some will go out to work or to day centres during the day. In some homes, there is a limit to the length of time an individual can live there—obviously, both carer and patient need to know about this.

Some accommodation is provided by people who let spare rooms in their houses to people recovering from mental illness. They may also provide cooked meals. Visits from social workers or CPNs usually have to be arranged separately, as does attendance at day-care facilities. Some landlords insist that lodgers are out of the house during the day. Some local authorities have lists of people who are willing to take in mentally ill lodgers and who have looked after them well in the past.

Local authorities do have a responsibility to provide accommodation for people leaving psychiatric hospitals if it is needed, provided they lived within their boundaries before they were admitted. This accommodation may be in another area, with the first authority **sponsoring** people to live there through a financial arrangement with the second authority. This system has been misused recently by local authorities in large cities sponsoring discharged mental patients to live in suburban areas or seaside resorts where they have no local links. This happens because some authorities have too few resources locally, but it tends to place a heavy burden on the services in the area where the clients end up. Many local authorities and voluntary organisations provide sheltered flats and bed-sitters. The accommodation may be purpose-built; or a number of flats in a block may be given over to people recovering from mental illnesses. Some support is given, sometimes by social workers or housing officers, sometimes by voluntary-sector helpers. This may be an ideal arrangement for some mentally ill people.

A variety of charitable organisations are involved in the creation of accommodation for former hospital patients. These include the Richmond Fellowship, the Mental After-Care Association, the Psychiatric Rehabilitation Association and several local branches of MIND. A lot of housing associations also provide 'special needs' accommodation that can be used for those with mental health problems.

The decision that individuals shall move from home into one of these facilities should be a joint one by them, the relatives they live with, and the clinical team.

People who have longstanding psychiatric problems may require particular services to **rehabilitate** them, to help them get started again after having been mentally ill. This may include relearning old skills, such as working to a routine; or acquiring new skills, as required for some particular job; or new interests such as painting or pottery. It may also mean helping clients to regain the confidence needed to go back out into the community. This is usually a very gradual process—certainly not one that can be hurried—so that staff may see it in terms of months or years, particularly for someone who has had several bouts of illness.

Many rehabilitation services provide a working environment that includes facilities specially designed to help mentally ill people, but some are more general and available to other members of the public. Nowadays most of these sheltered workshops are provided by local charities, although they may be paid for by social services.

Some hospitals incorporate a **day hospital**, to which patients come during the day from their homes. Here the emphasis is very much on rehabilitation. Occasionally, the day hospital may be seen as an alternative to full-time admission, but usually it is used by recently discharged patients. It will often have its own occupational therapy and sheltered workshops (the principles of sheltered work are described in more detail on p. 117). It may be a good idea for you to ask about the local facilities available for someone recovering from severe mental illness, as they vary considerably around the country. It is probably best to ask the local social services department about this when they do a needs assessment, but your key worker should also know what is available.

There are also **day centres**, provided by local authorities. No local authority, however, has yet set up the number of day centres required by government guidelines, and some have set up none at all. The activities in day centres are not very different from those in day hospitals, but the level of supervision is lower. You can obtain information about the range of local authority provisions for the mentally ill from your local social services department.

When we first started to work with mentally ill people, a normal aim of treatment and rehabilitation was that they should return to full-time employment. Even now, people who suffer from the more minor psychiatric disorders assume that they will go back to their jobs when they are better. However, times have changed for those who become more seriously ill, particularly with a disorder like schizophrenia which often impairs performance even when the more acute symptoms have abated. Many of these people either never return to outside employment, or have infrequent temporary jobs.

Nevertheless, there are facilities that are geared towards helping mental patients return to employment, and that recognise that this may be a long process. Some are run by statutory authorities, some by voluntary agencies. Attendance may involve getting back into a previous work routine—for instance, factory or clerical work—or retraining for some new occupation.

The facilities that may sometimes play a role in rehabilitating particular individuals recovering from mental illness include local authority rehabilitation and assessment centres, community-based industrial units, sheltered industrial groups, employment rehabilitation centres, skill centres, job clubs, residential training colleges and colleges of further education.

Organisations that provide employment include Remploy, the Psychiatric Rehabilitation Association, the Richmond Fellowship, some local branches of MIND and the National Schizophrenia Fellowship. As well as training and rehabilitation, these organisations provide guidance on many aspects of the return to open employment (see Appendix 2 for details). But if your relative doesn't manage to make the transfer to a job in the outside world, sheltered employment may become a reasonable and rewarding option.

Many people who have recovered from a mental illness and are returning to the hurly-burly of the employment market will initially need additional help. This can be obtained from the Disablement Resettlement Officer (DRO), who works in your local Job Centre. In this country any firm that employs more than twenty people must reserve 3 per cent of its posts for persons who are registered as disabled. This may help your relative in getting a job—it is the DRO's responsibility to consider placing someone on the Disabled Persons' Register. However, there is often a long waiting-list for reserved posts.

Sometimes it may be possible for a client to get practical guidance on the frequently harrowing business of attending job interviews. This may be provided by professionals from the organisation that is helping to get him or her back into employment, or it can be obtained from the psychologist or occupational therapist on the mental health team, or by attending a job club provided by a local charity.

People who become mentally ill may lose their job, but mental illness on its own is not grounds for dismissal. If your relative's employer wanted to dismiss him or her, he would need to ask for a medical report to be provided concerning his or her fitness to work. If the doctor providing the report was of the opinion that your relative would not be able to work again for a year, the employer would then be in a position to dismiss him or her. He could also do so for poor performance at work, if this was apparent. However, an employer cannot dismiss someone for either of these reasons without giving warning, and an individual has in any case the right to appeal to an industrial tribunal if he or she does so within three months.

If this is the position faced by your relative, MIND's legal advice department (at head office) can offer advice about the legal position over dismissal on grounds of mental illness.

Dealing with mental health professionals

If you live with someone who has had a severe mental illness, you will almost inevitably come into close and perhaps frequent contact with mental health staff. Unfortunately, these relationships are often uncomfortable for both sides. This may sometimes make obtaining treatment or help for your relative or for yourself more difficult than it need be, and may even impair the patient's progress. It is extremely important that you should not be intimidated in your interviews with mental health staff. Do not be dissuaded from asking any questions you want to, or from expressing concern over what worries you.

Often, these staff–relative relationships start badly because of an upsetting hospital admission that relatives, clients and even staff may afterwards feel has not been handled properly. If your first introduction to the local mental health facilities involves following your screaming relative down a corridor late at night, accompanied by police, subsequent relationships may be difficult. Such scenes are fairly rare, but if someone has developed a serious mental illness and is unwilling to be seen by a psychiatrist, or refuses to go to hospital, the result may be a crisis that is very unpleasant and shocking for all concerned. Sometimes, such crises happen very suddenly and are quite unavoidable, but it is natural to want to blame someone, and clinical staff may be a convenient, and sometimes justified, target.

After your relative has been admitted, staff will usually want to ask you many questions about his or her early history, the existence of any problems in the past and intimate details about any relationships—and sometimes, if it is relevant, about yours too. The clinical staff see it as necessary to obtain the maximum amount of information about a client as quickly as possible after an admission, and a relative is normally the best person to provide it. However, relatives often feel that these questions are unnecessarily intrusive, as well as endlessly repeated. To an extent, this situation arises because the psychiatric team are properly careful about not jumping to conclusions, and they need to use the kind of detailed information and observation that relatives can supply in order to shape their decisions. Relatives may also think that the situation is unfairly one-sided, if their own questions are not answered. But even these days some professionals have particular difficulties in talking openly with relatives. This is, of course, crazy—if a mental health professional cannot feel easy in talking to people, who can?—but, unfortunately, it is still sometimes the case. Some professionals still have particular difficulties in admitting that they do not know the answer to a given question, though relatives have a right to know this.

The staff's assessment of a patient, of what treatment will be best and of how he or she will respond to it, usually takes some time to complete, and may indeed continue to change as more information becomes available. This delay can be frustrating for you as a relative, particularly if the psychiatric team hesitate, as they often do, after admission or initial assessment before deciding on the best treatments. And even then, they may be hesitant or even evasive about telling you of their decisions. It should at least be clear among the team members who is responsible for saying what to whom, but all the same it may still be quite hard for you to squeeze out of them any authoritative statement about what is wrong with your relative. Instant answers to insistent questions may not be available. Staff may simply not know the answers, or they may be reluctant to risk upsetting relatives by being too pessimistic. Unfortunately, it is impossible to be sure about the likely course of a severe episode of mental illness—which may account for some of the reticence that relatives encounter. While we know that some patients will recover completely, it may not be possible at the outset to recognise who those patients are. But general information, if not specific, should be available.

Clearly, though, if you feel you are not getting the information you need, you must make this plain to the staff, particularly as they now have a clear duty to keep you informed and involved. It is perfectly reasonable for you to ask to speak to the consultant psychiatrist or other members of the clinical team to discuss their views on your relative's problems, the sorts of treatment available, what can be expected on the patient's return home, and the staff members' opinions on the sort of mental illness it is and how your relative seems to be doing.

If a **social worker** is involved in your relative's care, he or she may be particularly useful to you here, since social workers, as mentioned earlier, often take a special interest in the family as a whole. Their viewpoint can be a major helpful addition to information obtained from other members of staff. The way to contact social workers differs from hospital to hospital. Sometimes a 'referral' has to be made by the psychiatric team. Elsewhere it is less formal—nursing staff should be able to advise you on how to contact the social worker, or you can phone the local social services department yourself.

It is often useful to have more than one appointment with the mental health staff, as it may be impossible for you to ask all your questions and remember all the answers during an initial interview. Don't be afraid to take a notebook along so that you can write down what you are being told, or to ask for explanations if unfamiliar technical terms are used. Do not hide from your ill relative the fact of your appointment—it is, after all, perfectly reasonable for you to want to find out as much as possible about his or her illness—but how much you reveal about what was said will depend on the particular circumstances.

Not all the problems encountered in trying to gather information are due to the uncertainty of the situation or the inadequacies of the staff. It is quite possible to be told a thing, yet not really take it on board, especially if the experience is novel and you are distressed by it. It usually takes time, much more time than with a straightforward physical illness, for carers to grasp exactly what is happening to their relative. It may be many months before you come to an understanding of some of the causes—which even the staff may be unsure of—and are able to accept some of the long-term implications of a severe mental illness for your relative and for the family as a whole.

Again, particularly if this is your relative's first major illness, you are likely to experience a range of **emotions** at this difficult time. You may feel that staff don't consult you over treatment decisions or give you adequate support, and even that they are blaming you for your relative's problems. You may well feel very confused and worried about the future. It is usually a great relief that someone else is now coping with him or her for a while, but such feelings may also make you feel very guilty. Other feelings that people in your position have described include inadequacy, hopelessness, bitterness that these things have happened at all, and great upset that the patient has become so ill. It is not surprising that the attempts of staff and relatives to communicate with each other at this time are often unsuccessful.

Many find that **self-help groups** provide a useful place for carers to obtain information and exchange experiences. One such organisation is the National Schizophrenia Fellowship, which is described in some detail on pp. 122–3. If you are going through a bad patch, talking to relatives who have been through it all before can be a great help, and you in turn may be able to help others at a later date. Professional people can be invited to speak to such a group from time to time, and to answer questions.

Second opinions

In the National Health Service, it is accepted that people will sometimes want another opinion, from another doctor. If your relative wants such a **second opinion**, he or she must find a doctor willing to cooperate, and there is no obligation on any given doctor to do this. Usually the doctor in charge of the case will be agreeable to someone seeking a second opinion, and there will be no difficulty in doing so. Your relative may do this entirely through your family doctor, but if he or she discovers a psychiatrist willing to see him or her, the GP will probably agree to make a formal referral.

There may occasionally be particular problems for psychiatric patients who want to be referred for the opinion of another doctor. Psychiatric hospitals are responsible for all the people living in a particular area, and these **catchment areas** are usually rigidly observed because it is felt that this ensures the best service for all those with mental health problems who live there. So it may be difficult to obtain the opinion of a doctor working in a hospital that deals with another area. And a possible problem with getting a second opinion from a doctor at the same hospital as the client's own is that all the doctors there are likely to work closely together, so that he or she may feel, with some justification, that a second opinion from a close colleague of the first doctor might be prejudiced. Furthermore, the psychiatrist may be tempted to feel that the client's reluctance to accept a first opinion is due to his or her psychiatric state.

The situation for the mentally ill is therefore sometimes unsatisfactory. One way round this particular problem is to seek a second opinion from a psychiatrist in a hospital with a medical school (a **teaching hospital**), because the services that teaching hospitals provide are not usually restricted to their catchment area. There are many such hospitals in London, and most large cities have one. The disadvantage of this method of obtaining a second opinion is that it may involve travelling quite a distance. Your GP can make the referral, although it is useful if you or your relative can supply the name of a doctor you would like to consult at the given hospital. However, the Royal College of

Psychiatrists makes it a rule *not* to give out the names of suitable psychiatrists, so you would have to find a name for yourself. These days a second-opinion referral like this involves the transfer of NHS money, as it is an 'extra contractual referral' (ECR). If your family doctor is a fund-holder he or she can pay the service providing the opinion; otherwise, it is done by arrangement with the FHSA. This procedure has made family doctors reluctant to make second-opinion referrals, but you are entitled to insist, and to approach the FHSA directly if your GP doesn't want to.

It is, of course, possible to seek a further opinion **privately**—that is, outside the National Health Service—which you or your relative will have to pay for. Your doctor may know a psychiatrist who sees patients in this way. Any long-term private medical treatment is very expensive indeed, particularly if it involves frequent hospital in-patient treatment, but you may feel that a one-off appointment for a second opinion is worth paying for if it sets your mind at rest. Private medical insurance schemes are unlikely to cover long-term psychiatric care.

Detained patients (see p. 124) have the right to a second opinion under the Mental Health Act, and the Mental Health Act Commission has the duty of appointing a doctor to provide this second opinion.

Other sources of support

We have given advice on how you can best set about obtaining what you need for your relative and yourself from the psychiatric services. There are, though, still places in this country where local facilities are underfunded or underdeveloped, or the local professionals are apathetic, ignorant, unsympathetic or just plain overworked. Sometimes, by means of great efforts, you may be able to browbeat them into extending the provision they offer to you and your relative. But in some circumstances no adequate service will be forthcoming, try as you might, and you may have to turn to independent organisations such as the **National Schizophrenia Fellowship**, the **Manic Depression Fellowship** or **MIND**. Such organisations offer information and support, and they can also often exert pressure on services to develop local facilities or to be more responsive to your needs.

There is now an **advocacy** service available for clients, if services are felt to be inadequate, which is usually linked to hospitals and to the local hospital administration. Or, again, the social services or your mental health team should be able to advise you on how to ask them to act for you in order to elicit what you or your relative feels is a reasonable service. If all else fails, each hospital Trust now has to make clear what its complaints procedure is. Once a complaint has been made, a hospital Trust has to respond, investigate it and reply. If you are still not satisfied, your local MP, if he can be persuaded that there is a case to answer, can take up a particular issue or incident on your behalf.

5 Treatment

There are several treatments that are offered routinely for severe mental illness in NHS hospitals in all parts of the country. These may include **admission** to hospital, **physical treatments** like drug therapy, and, occasionally, electroconvulsive therapy (ECT), as well as various **social treatments**. They are all described below. Private medical care tends to offer a similar approach.

ADMISSION TO HOSPITAL

If your relative has just become ill with severe depression, mania or schizophrenia, he or she is likely to be offered **hospital admission**. Though this does not on the face of it seem to be a form of treatment, removing people from a situation where they have been overwhelmed by worries and stresses may well cause their symptoms to diminish. Rest, routine and nursing care all add to the beneficial effects of being in hospital. At its best, a psychiatric ward provides a relatively neutral environment where an individual's symptoms and behaviour can be assessed, usually over a period of several weeks.

You and your relative may, however, find such an admission very upsetting, especially if it is the first time he or she has been admitted and the ward is noisy. Not infrequently, though, patients find this less upsetting than family at this moment. When a person has been advised that he or she should be admitted to hospital, but refuses, the psychiatrist may sometimes decide that it is in the patient's interest to be admitted 'under a Section'—that is, without his or her consent, through the powers of the Mental Health Act (see pp. 124–37). While relatives usually see the necessity of compulsory admission, they may, quite understandably, be distressed. Some may be left feeling very guilty, as if they have 'betrayed' the patient. In addition, you yourself may never have visited a psychiatric ward before. Psychiatric hospitals, and mental illness itself, are still seen as frightening or shameful by many people. There is often a suspicion, unfortunately confirmed by the more lurid films and TV programmes, that once you enter a psychiatric hospital it is difficult to get out again, and that the people there are bizarre and terrifying.

The reality is more commonplace, and mental hospitals have, in any case, changed considerably, especially since the 1950s; very few of the older hospitals remain open. Nevertheless, some still retain a forbidding exterior or are located in an isolated position, which can take some time to get used to. As mentioned earlier, most psychiatric facilities are now based in district general hospitals, and this may make an admission easier to accept and more convenient. Of course, if it is not the first time a patient has been admitted, both relative and patient will know more about what they are going to have to deal with.

You may find it hard to visit your relative in hospital, perhaps because of practical inconvenience, perhaps because you don't really relish the ward environment. Nevertheless, your relative will very probably set great store by your visits, so try to go as often as possible. Apart from the requirements of ward activities such as occupational therapy (see pp 116–17), visiting is usually fairly unrestricted. When you visit, it will normally be all right to go for a walk or out to a local café with your relative, but do tell the nursing staff what you are doing and when you will be back.

'PHYSICAL' TREATMENT

Drugs in mental illness

Effective treatments in psychiatry are of fairly recent date. Before the 1950s, psychiatrists had little to offer their patients except sedation and nursing care. If people got better, it was usually the result of the natural ebb and flow of their illness. However, around that time there were a number of innovations, which included ECT, the first drugs effective against schizophrenia and depression, and the development of techniques of rehabilitation. Elderly clinicians who can remember those times will tell you how dramatic the effect of introducing these new treatments really was—it became possible to empty whole wards. Nowadays, the rate of improvement is much slower. Many of the new drugs that have come out recently are really variations on themes established in the 1950s. Usually, they represent improvements not because they are any more effective in making people better, but because they have less in the way of side effects. When we carp at the use and possible overuse of medication in psychiatry, it is worth remembering that dramatic beginning.

New drug treatments in psychiatry arise because a pharmaceutical company develops a new preparation, which must be subjected to very careful testing to establish its effectiveness and its freedom from side effects before it is granted a licence and can be prescribed in the normal way.

Most people will be offered some sort of drug treatment during their hospital admission. Although drugs are never the complete answer to a mental illness, they are often a necessary first step, providing a platform on which other types of treatment can build. In the treatment of psychiatric conditions, medication is often continued after a person returns home, sometimes for many months or years. Many people have expressed worries that psychiatrists use drugs merely in order to keep patients quiet, and that large doses are prescribed without proper consideration of their possible bad effects. There are some grounds for this worry, but most psychiatrists these days weigh the benefits and disadvantages of treatment carefully. Nevertheless, if you feel that you see changes in your relative that might be due to the unwanted effects of medication, it is reasonable to share your worry with the psychiatrist in charge of treatment. It needs to be borne in mind, though, that such changes can be the result, not of the drugs, but of the underlying illness. This section will describe the **sorts of effects** that may arise from taking the drugs that psychiatrists commonly use.

One of the problems with drugs in this country is that they all have at least two names. This can be confusing. First is the approved, or 'generic', name of the compound—such as diazepam and amitriptyline. Then the pharmaceutical companies give their product their own name, which is different—so diazepam becomes Valium and amitriptyline Tryptizol. (The company name is distinguished from the generic name by having a capital initial letter.) If, as sometimes happens, several companies each have their own brand name for a drug, the picture becomes very complicated indeed. Doctors are encouraged to use the generic names, but they often don't. In this book, we are quite inconsistent about it—we go for the name you are most likely to have come across.

There are several different sorts of medication that may be prescribed for the severe mental illnesses we are concerned with here. Some are given in tablet or capsule form, or as a syrup, while others, the **long-acting** ones, can be given by injection weekly or less frequently. Many people end up preferring the long-acting medication, simply because it has to be taken less often and they don't have to worry about remembering when it's time for their tablets. On the other hand, it does mean that some of the control over his or her medication is taken from the patient, as the drug remains in the body for a few weeks after the last injection. Some patients find this unacceptable.

Schizophrenia is usually treated with **major tranquillisers**. Examples you may have heard of include Largactil, Serenace and Modecate, but there are now many others available. We list these in Tables 1, 2 and 3. Acute attacks of mania are also usually treated with medicines from this group.

The major tranquillisers are so called because of their effects on severe psychiatric disturbance. The **minor tranquillisers**, such as Valium, work in a different way and are used for different conditions. The major tranquillisers do calm the patient down, but their particular effect is to reduce the more disturbing symptoms, such as hallucinations, odd ideas and difficulties in thinking. In most people this means that the more severe problems of the illness can be controlled, but it may not mean that they disappear completely, or that the drugs are effective all the time. While the major tranquillisers are often very effective in treating the more dramatic features of the illness, they have little effect on **negative symptoms** (see p. 28). Unlike the minor tranquillisers, the major tranquillisers do not seem to be addictive.

It is also true that the drugs do not necessarily make a schizophrenic or manic patient 'feel better'. During a straightforward physical illness like an infection, it is usually quickly obvious that medication reduces fever and improves well-being. In contrast, drugs used for these severe mental illnesses may have no effects discernible to the patient, who may even feel worse for

TABLE 1
Major tranquillisers

DRUG	PROPRIETARY NAME	MORE COMMON SIDE EFFECTS
chlorpromazine	Largactil	Blurred vision
chlorprothixene	Taractan	Constipation
droperidol	Droleptan	Difficulty in passing
flupenthixol	Depixol	water
fluphenazine	Moditen	Dry mouth
haloperidol	Haldol	Faintness on suddenly
	Serenace	standing up
loxapine	Loxapac	Increased appetite
methotrimeprazine	Nozinan	Increased effect of
oxypertine	Integrin	alcohol
pericyazine	Neulactil	Loss of facial
perphenazine	Fentazin	expression
pimozide	Orap	Lowering of body
prochloroperazine	Stemetil	temperature
promazine	Sparine	Odd movements of body and face
sulpiride	Dolmatil	Restlessness
	Sulparex	Sensitivity of skin
	Sulpitil	to sunlight
thiopropazate	Dartalan	Stiffness
thioridazine	Melleril	Tremor
trifluoroperazine	Stelazine	
trifluperidol	Triperidol	
zuclopenthixol	Clopixol	

Not every drug shows all of these effects to the same extent. Side effects are often temporary.

a time. This is because it may take some days or weeks before the benefits of major tranquillisers become apparent—adequate levels of the drug in the body are reached only gradually. And to someone who does not agree that there is anything wrong with him or her, being given drugs that seem unnecessary can be very disturbing.

You too may find this issue very difficult, if you are unable to see any immediate benefits of the drug treatment. Often, though, relatives can see quite clearly that the patient's refusal to take

TABLE 2
Major tranquillisers given by injection

DRUG	PROPRIETARY NAME
clopenthixol decanoate	Clopixol
flupenthixol decanoate	Depixol
fluphenazine decanoate	Modecate
haloperidol decanoate	Haldol decanoate
pipothiazine palmitate	Piportil depot

Side effects are similar to those when medication is given by mouth.

the drugs has a bad effect on the course of the illness. Their help in encouraging patients to take their drugs can be crucial.

The medication can then work to help the patient become gradually more in touch with reality and easier to talk to.

Most medicines have several effects. The unwanted ones—the **side effects**—of the major tranquillisers may include dry mouth and weight gain (see Tables 1, 2 and 3). In addition, they can produce symptoms rather like those of Parkinson's disease—slowing, restlessness, trembling and muscle stiffness. This is referred to as 'drug-induced Parkinsonism'. However, these side effects usually pass off in a few weeks, and other tablets can be taken to reduce them.

There is a continuing concern over the issue of 'tardive dyskinesia', a movement disorder which comes on after many months' or years' treatment with major tranquillisers. The most prominent and frequent effect is a continual grimacing, which the poor sufferer usually seems unaware of. Treatments for this condition have generally been ineffective—it doesn't normally get better, although some people are helped by switching to the new tranquilliser, clozapine (Table 3). To complicate the issue, it is not entirely clear that it *is* a drug side effect: such grimacings were described in schizophrenia long before major tranquillisers existed, and are still sometimes reported in those who have not yet been prescribed these drugs.

For most patients an optimal balance can be achieved between the untoward effects and the beneficial 'calming down' effects of the tranquillising drugs. However, patients who are not convinced of the benefits can become very concerned with the side effects, and may refuse to take any medication at all. Unfortunately, this sometimes means the initial illness returns. Just as they take some time to build up a **therapeutic effect**, the drugs often take some days or weeks to wear off. This means that there may be no immediate change when patients stop taking them, so they may feel their decision was justified.

David, aged twenty-two, was admitted to hospital because he was acutely disturbed. He had been rushing out of his house, shouting at passers-by and telling them to leave him alone. He thought they were spying on him and that there was an evil and complicated plot afoot to harm him. He continued to be upset in hospital and was given Largactil, at first in moderate doses; but when this did not have any effect, he was given quite large doses. Over a period of a few days he settled down and became less frightened. Gradually he lost his delusional ideas and was able to take part in the ward activities. He did become quite shaky for about ten days, almost certainly as a result of the Largactil. But this wore off without the need either to reduce the dose or to give further medication to neutralise it. After about eight weeks he was discharged, but it was felt that he should continue to take medication, although in much lower doses. In fact he still takes it, and it seems to have been effective in preventing the return of his frightening persecutory ideas. He did discontinue it for a few weeks, but was strongly advised to start it again when he had a minor return of his old suspiciousness.

David does not like to talk about the ideas he had, giving the impression that this is because he thinks they show him in rather a foolish light. His experience with medication was a reasonably happy one, and he has no objection to continuing with it. He does appear to think of medication as a small price to pay to prevent the return of his unwelcome thoughts.

Clearly, though, not all sufferers are equally happy with medication. For some, this will be because they think they never needed it or, at any rate, no longer need it; for others it is because their medication has side effects that they don't like. In some very severe cases of schizophrenia, the psychiatrist may prescribe medication in the hope of only marginal benefit, trading off unpleasant side effects against the anguish that could be caused to the sufferer by letting his or her problems get out of control. This can be a very fine judgement, and there is no doubt that psychiatrists sometimes get it wrong: they have a tendency to err on the cautious side, although these days they are becoming more wary of the dangers of doing harm with the use of the major tranquillisers.

Given that the advantages and disadvantages of any one drug have to be so carefully weighed up, it might happen that you see things differently from your relative's psychiatrist. This may, of course, be because either you or the sufferer does not have all the information against which the correct prescription of medication must be judged. But if you feel strongly about it, talking to the psychiatrist will at least clear the air, and may lead to a modification of treatment.

It is in fact possible for some people with schizophrenia, even of a fairly enduring type, to manage without medication, although this may be at the cost of a more restricted lifestyle by which they avoid overstimulation. Provided they are not actually a danger to themselves or to others, this is a choice they have a right to make—although it may sometimes make things harder for those who look after them, both relatives and clinicians.

Since we wrote the first edition of this book there have been advances in the drug treatment of schizophrenia, and you may have heard of some of these (see Table 3). Clozapine (Clozaril) is actually quite an old drug that was originally discontinued because, as we describe below, it had—and still has—one particularly severe, if fairly rare, side effect. It acts somewhat differently from the other drugs in this field, having little in the way of the usual side effects such as shaking and other movement disorders. Indeed, it can be prescribed as a means of reducing these side effects. Its great benefit is that it is effective in about 50 per cent of those people who do not recover much in response to the other drugs. We have seen very disabled clients become much more able to look after themselves as a result of switching to clozapine.

But the big disadvantage of clozapine is that it causes a serious reduction in the number of white cells in the blood in perhaps 1–2 per cent of the people who take it, which prevents them from fighting infections properly. A few cases have died as a result. For this reason, people on clozapine have to have blood taken—at first weekly, then fortnightly, and eventually monthly—to make sure their white blood cell level is satisfactory.

TABLE 3
New major tranquillisers

DRUG	PROPRIETARY NAME	SIDE EFFECTS
clozapine	Clozaril	Does not produce shaking, stiffness or abnormal movements. Sometimes works where other drugs fail. Needs monitoring with a regular blood test—may cause a dangerous drop in white blood cells. Other side effects include drowsiness, drooling, weight gain and epileptic fits.
sertindole	Serdolect	Only rarely produces shaking, stiffness or abnormal movements. Can be taken once daily. May produce dry mouth, blurred vision, dizziness and weight gain. Because it has effects on the heart, it should not be given to those with heart disease. Patients should have an ECG (heart trace) before starting on it, and have their blood pressure checked while taking it.
risperidone	Risperdol	Only rarely produces shaking, stiffness or abnormal movements. Can be taken once daily. Makes some people anxious, others sleepy. May cause weight gain, stomach upsets and dizziness.
olanzapine	Zyprexa	Only rarely produces shaking, stiffness or abnormal movements. Can be taken once daily. May cause sleepiness, weight gain, dry mouth, blurred vision and dizziness.

These all represent an advance on earlier drugs, in spite of side effects (particularly of clozapine and sertindole). They are all very expensive, but one would probably want one's own relative to be given a drug from this group.

If the level starts to fall beyond a certain point, the clozapine has to be stopped. This side effect has two consequences in everybody who takes the drug: the blood tests are an inconvenience, and the drug is very expensive because the cost of these tests has to be covered. In addition, clozapine can be given only by mouth, not by long-acting injection. This means that people reluctant to take medication anyway may default on taking it. The other unusual side effect is a tendency to produce too much saliva, particularly at night. People on clozapine may wake to find their pillow drenched. This side effect does wear off, though, and can be reduced by reducing the dose of the drug.

Risperidone is another new medication, which is not quite as effective as clozapine, but like clozapine it probably works in some people who do not respond to the older drugs. It too is expensive, but does not affect the white blood cells, so no blood test is required. It has few side effects, and if it were not so dear most psychiatrists would probably use it as the first-choice drug.

Information on olanzapine and sertindole is given in Table 3, and there are other new drugs about to be introduced. The search is on for the 'son of clozapine'—a drug with all its advantages but without an effect on the white blood cells. It is not clear that any of the coming drugs fit this description.

Depression can be treated with **antidepressants**, of which there are three main groups. Over the last forty years the most commonly used group has been the **tricyclic antidepressants**, which includes drugs such as Tofranil, Tryptizol, Prothiaden and Ludiomil (see Table 4). Again, there are many for the doctor to choose from. In addition, a new group of drugs, which go by the appealing name of 'selective serotonin reuptake inhibitors' (SSRIs), have been developed since the first edition of this book. They are increasingly chosen because they have much less in the way of side effects than the tricyclic antidepressants, and they are probably now used just as frequently. They are all expensive. The most famous of these to the general public is Prozac. Another group, the **monoamine oxidase inhibitors** (MAOIs, Tables 5 and 6), includes Nardil and Parnate but is used less often. Also, a new 'reversible' MAOI has now been developed (moclobemide), which is likely to be a useful addition to the list of antidepressants.

Antidepressants are quite effective in restoring the **chemical imbalance** thought to underlie both moderate and severe

TABLE 4
Tricyclic antidepressants

DRUG	PROPRIETARY NAME	COMMON SIDE EFFECTS
amitriptyline	Tryptizol Lentizol	Dry mouth Blurred vision Constipation Difficulty in passing water Weight gain Confusion in the elderly Occasional worsening of symptoms in those with schizophrenia Increased effect of alcohol
amoxapine	Asendis	
clomipramine	Anafranil	
desipramine	Pertofran	
dothiepin	Prothiaden	
doxepin	Sinequan	
imipramine	Tofranil	
lofepramine	Gamanil	
maprotilene	Ludiomil	
nortriptyline	Allegron	
protriptyline	Concordin	
trazodone	Molipaxin	
trimipramine	Surmontil	

Side effects tend to wear off over a few days and are less prominent if the dose is gradually *increased to full levels.*

TABLE 5
Irreversible MAOI antidepressants

DRUG	PROPRIETARY NAME	COMMON SIDE EFFECTS
isocarboxazid	Marplan	Faintness on suddenly standing up Dangerous interactions with some other drugs Dangerous interactions with some foods (e.g., cheese) Increased effect of alcohol
phenelzine	Nardil	
tranylcypromine	Parnate	

Because of their interactions with other substances, these drugs are less commonly prescribed nowadays. In view of the introduction of moclobemide, they are likely to become even less popular.

TABLE 6
Reversible MAOI antidepressant

DRUG	PROPRIETARY NAME
moclobemide	Manerix

Much less likely than the older MAOIs to interact with food. Side effects are rare: sleep disturbance, dizziness, nausea and headache are occasionally experienced.

depression. It takes a few days before mood begins to lift, and the tablets have to be taken exactly as prescribed. It is likely to be several weeks, and in some cases even longer, before mood is completely normal, and the psychiatrist will probably continue to prescribe this medication for some time after that.

Antidepressants do have some immediate effects. Some make patients feel drowsy, while others may have an energising effect. This may interfere with the patient's ability to drive. Complaints of a dry mouth or of blurred vision are fairly common, but these side effects usually become less noticeable after a few days. The effects of **alcohol** are increased in people taking these drugs. The SSRIs only rarely have such side effects, although they have some of their own: they can increase anxiety for the first few days, and they can make some people feel quite nauseated. Nevertheless, they are usually more acceptable than the older tricyclic antidepressants. The irreversible MAOI group interact with certain foodstuffs that contain high levels of **tyramine**, particularly cheese. These reactions can be dangerous: there can be a rapid rise in blood pressure accompanied by severe headache. Very occasionally, the reaction can trigger a stroke. Patients prescribed this type of drug are given **cards** by the pharmacy listing all the foods to be avoided. This list is given in Table 7. The new drug from this group, moclobemide, very rarely interacts with tyramine, so no dietary restrictions are needed. And it has very few other side effects.

You will remember Susan, the depressed teacher we spoke of in Chapter 1. You might like to know what happened to her. She was suffering from the sort of depression that a psychiatrist would immediately recognise as likely to benefit from a tricyclic antidepressant. So she was prescribed Prothiaden, although she would

TABLE 7
Foods to be avoided by those taking irreversible monoamine oxidase inhibitors

Avocado pears
Broad beans
Cheese (especially cream cheese)
Chocolate, yoghurt, cream and game, which may produce a reaction, although more rarely
Food that might be 'going off' (especially meat, fish, poultry)
Meat and yeast extracts (e.g., Bovril, Marmite, Oxo)
Pickled herrings
Proprietary cough and cold medicines (i.e., bought over the counter at a pharmacist's).

The effects of alcohol are increased by these drugs, and, in addition, red wine can set off the same reaction as the foods above.

probably have responded equally to the other drugs in this group. At first she was given a small dose, but over a few days it was increased to a moderately large one. This gradual introduction of the drug was deliberate, because it lessens the chance of side effects. Susan did notice that her mouth was dry, and she felt a little bit unsteady and sleepy. In fact, since she was feeling pretty rotten anyway, the sleepiness did not matter and, if anything, took the edge off her anguish.

At first there was little change, but after a fortnight or so she was able to report a slight lightening of the gloom. Over the following few weeks she gradually improved, and after two months was able to return to work. She had started enjoying herself again. Her husband was delighted to have back the wife he had known—she was once more a sociable, loving and energetic woman. Apart from the antidepressant, little treatment was required beyond support through the bad period, and some advice about the general management of her life. The medication was continued for about three months after she had fully recovered. Just occasionally, someone who appears completely better may relapse if antidepressants are stopped too quickly.

Patients who suffer repeated episodes of depression, and especially those who have also experienced an episode of mania, may be prescribed **lithium**. While this does have an effect on acute symptoms, its main use is to make relapse less likely. It may take a year, or even more, before it can be seen to be effective, and it therefore involves patients taking medication while free of symptoms. From time to time the psychiatrist will want a **blood test** to determine the level of this drug in the body. This is to ensure the correct dose and an absence of side effects, as the correct dose lies in a fairly narrow band between one that is ineffective and one that produces unwanted effects. Monitoring ensures that only a tiny minority of patients suffer significant side effects. Nevertheless, it can sometimes happen that the level becomes too high. Symptoms that suggest this possibility are listed in Table 8.

Jeremy, a quiet scholarly man who worked in a bank, had experienced three rather damaging breakdowns. The first looked like schizophrenia, but by the time of the third it became clear that the likely diagnosis was manic depressive illness. His employers had been tolerant of his illness, despite the fact that his behaviour when ill had brought adverse publicity to them, but their tolerance could not be boundless. It was decided to start treatment with lithium. Jeremy has now taken it for ten years without any recurrence of illness; his only complaint is that he finds it hard to lose weight.

Gillian also did well on lithium. However, she developed considerable swelling of the ankles, and it was decided to take her off the medication. While this was sensible in terms of her physical condition, it did cause a return of symptoms from time to time

TABLE 8
Side effects of lithium

Early and fleeting	Nausea Diarrhoea Metallic taste	Mention to doctor. Not dangerous
Persistent	Weight gain	
	Shakiness Increased consumption of water Increased amounts of urine	Mention to doctor as a matter of urgency. It may be necessary to reduce the number of tablets

that led to her admission to hospital on two occasions, and caused considerable strain for her family.

Recently, it has been found that the drug **carbamazepine** can be used successfully to prevent the return of manic depressive symptoms, sometimes in people for whom other treatments have failed. Gillian was started on carbamazepine and has been well ever since. A number of other drugs have occasionally been used to help in mood stabilisation.

Sometimes, if an individual suffers from depressive delusions, the psychiatrist will prescribe major tranquillisers such as those used in schizophrenia. They can be quite effective in this condition, too. Occasionally, people with these illnesses may be given **minor tranquillisers** (see Tables 9 and 10), such as diazepam or lorazepam, known as benzodiazepines. These do not help to cure an attack directly, but may calm someone who is particularly agitated. Psychiatrists are increasingly reluctant to prescribe these drugs and will do so only in certain restricted circumstances, as they are now known to be **addictive**. When they *are* prescribed, the psychiatrist will these days aim to discontinue them as soon as possible—certainly within a few months, usually a few weeks. In some cases when people have been taking minor tranquillisers for years, it may be impracticable to discontinue them, especially if other problems seem more important. People aiming to come off these drugs after a long period should do so under medical supervision, because there may be **withdrawal effects**, especially if it is done too quickly. A list of the withdrawal effects is given in Table 11.

It is difficult for all concerned if a patient refuses to take prescribed medication. It may not be possible to convince the reluctant individual that medication is helpful until it has had some effect and he or she is sufficiently in touch with reality again to feel the benefit. People with manic depressive illness may refuse to take lithium because they actually miss feeling 'high'. Hopefully, with support from relatives, a sympathetic doctor will be able to work out the best and most acceptable drug dosage. This can often be gradually reduced as the patient improves.

There are some patients who are **not** helped despite being given very large doses of medication, and others who need to continue to take it for long periods without any obvious benefit but in order to prevent a recurrence of illness. In the early stages it is usually not possible to tell how a given person will respond

TABLE 9

Benzodiazepines: minor tranquillisers and hypnotics

DRUG	PROPRIETARY NAME	COMMON SIDE EFFECTS
alprazolam	Xanax	Drowsiness
bromazepam	Lexotan	Increased effect of
chlordiazepoxide	Librium	alcohol
clobazepam	Frisium	Addiction
clorazepate	Tranxene	Confusion
diazepam	Diazemuls	Impaired performance on
	Stesolid	physical tasks such as
	Valium	driving, working
	Valclair	machinery
flunitrazepam	Rohypnol	
flurazepam	Dalmane	
loprazolam		
lorazepam	Ativan	
lormetazepam		
nitrazepam	Mogadon	
oxazepam		
temazepam	Normison	

TABLE 10

Other hypnotics and tranquillisers

Hypnotics DRUG	PROPRIETARY NAME	COMMON SIDE EFFECTS
zolpidem	Zimovane	These are new and
zopiclone	Stilnoct	probably represent
		an advance
		Stomach upset
		Stomach upset,
		dizziness, headache

Tranquilliser DRUG	PROPRIETARY NAME	
buspirone	Buspar	Dizziness, headache,
		nausea; possibly not
		addictive

TABLE 11
Withdrawal symptoms of benzodiazepines

Apprehension and anxiety
Faintness, light-headedness or unsteadiness
Fatigue
Hypsersensitivity to sensation (especially light and sound)
Loss of appetite
Pins and needles
Shakiness, muscle twitches, leg cramps
Sleep disturbance
Vomiting

These symptoms are likely to come on a few days after stopping the medication, usually only after appreciable doses have been taken for six months or so. In some instances the symptoms may appear like flu or gastroenteritis, or may, except for the muscle twitches, resemble an anxiety state.

to drug treatment, or how long he or she will need to take it. To allow for this, the doctor will keep a close eye on the medication, and may vary it from time to time.

Occasionally, you or your relative may feel that the doctor is issuing repeat prescriptions without properly assessing the need for them. This impression *may* be accurate, but it sometimes arises because of a lack of communication. In either case, it is reasonable for you to seek an opportunity to express your concern to the doctor in order to clarify the situation.

Problems with taking medication

It may happen that you suspect that your mentally ill relative is not telling the truth about taking his or her tablets. In this difficult situation, it is probably not a good idea to try immediate confrontation. One reasonable course of action is to accompany your relative to his or her next appointment with a member of the clinical team. Ask to see the team member separately, and explain the problem; alternatively, phone him or her about it. Suggest that you might to some extent supervise your relative's drug treatment. (To do this, you obviously need to be very clear about the correct dosage, when the medication is to be taken, and the likelihood of any side effects.) You can then tell your relative that the clinical staff want you to help with medication. You can remind him or her when the tablets are due, and watch them being taken.

Having established your right to take an interest in this way, it may then also be possible to raise the question of the tablet you find down the toilet, or of the bottle fuller than it should be. Clearly, how you handle this depends on your relationship and whether the necessary frankness can be tolerated. It will not be useful if all you manage to change is the method of disposal!

ECT (electroconvulsive therapy)

This is sometimes referred to as 'shock treatment', an unfortunate name that is bound to frighten both patients and relatives. So it's important for you to know something about it, should it be offered. ECT has caused considerable controversy, both within the psychiatric profession and among members of the public. There is no doubt at all that in the past it was used too frequently and in cases where benefit was unlikely. On the other hand, in those days psychiatrists had little to offer in the way of effective physical treatment, and so may have sometimes used it where there was only the remotest hope that it would work. Nowadays it is used quite rarely. For carefully chosen patients it can be a most effective treatment, and in the severest depression or mania it may be life-saving. Elderly people are more likely to have depressive illness of a degree to warrant ECT.

It is most commonly used in **manic depressive illness**, particularly **severe depression**, and especially if the sufferer has **delusions**.

Before a patient is given ECT, the treatment is explained and he or she is then asked to sign a **consent form** (which is invalid unless the explanation has been given). Only in special circumstances may ECT be given if the patient refuses or if he or she is too ill to give proper consent (see p. 134).

The procedure is carefully controlled. The patient lies on a bed and is given a special **short-acting anaesthetic** and a **muscle relaxant**. A small electric current is then passed through the brain via electrodes applied to the head, and it sets off a sort of epileptic fit. Such fits result from a simultaneous discharge of the nerve cells of the brain, which necessarily involves the release of **transmitter substances**. This seems to restore the **chemical imbalance** in the brain thought to be responsible for manic depressive illness. For improvement to occur, it is necessary that a fit should take place—the mere passage of electricity is not sufficient.

The muscle relaxant is used to prevent the normal movement of muscles that accompanies an epileptic fit, and thereby eliminates the risk of injury. When a muscle relaxant is given, the fit is almost imperceptible—not at all like the lurid portrayals in early films of the patient shaking violently on a bed. In fact, there may be some difficulty in deciding if the fit has occurred—the only signs may be the merest twitch of the eyebrows or of the big toe. ECT given with a relaxant in this way is called 'modified ECT', and is the only method in routine use in this country.

The patient recovers consciousness within minutes. After having the treatment he or she may have trouble remembering things, but the effect will nearly always be temporary. This memory disturbance tends to be seen more in elderly people; a few patients may feel sick or suffer from headache or a stiff neck. Although some patients need less, the usual practice is to give eight to twelve shocks with a few days between shocks.

ECT is occasionally given to **out-patients**. If your relative is offered it, he or she will be told not to drink anything for some hours beforehand. This is because an anaesthetic is given. After the treatment patients will be somewhat confused but will recover quickly. After an hour or so and a cup of tea, they will be ready to be taken home, by car or public transport. In a few hours they will be back to normal, except for a difficulty in remembering things that may last a few days.

Sometimes, individual shocks have a marked effect in combating depression, but that effect partly wears off before the next shock is due. Recovery in such cases follows a pattern of 'two steps forward, one step back'. Relatives should not worry about this rather jerky progress.

Over the years there has been a lot of research on ECT. Although we don't know the precise details of how it works, we do know a lot about its effects and the indications for its use. It has been shown to be a **safe** and **effective** treatment for very severe depression that does not respond to other physical treatment. Psychiatrists use it because it may be the quickest way to reduce the patient's suffering or to remove the risk of suicide. It can be used safely in the very old as well as in those who are quite ill physically. It is now rarely prescribed for schizophrenia because the major tranquillisers are used instead, although it is effective in the very rare form called catatonic stupor.

One of the main, although still relatively rare, complaints that patients make about ECT is that it impairs their memory. Again, there has been considerable research into this. When people who have had ECT in the past are given memory tests, there is no evidence of impairment—they are as good at remembering things as people who have not had ECT. So why do they say that their memory is not as good as it was? There are indeed **short-lived effects** on memory, lasting perhaps a few weeks at most, and it is possible that some people just find it hard to realise that these have disappeared. Also, those who feel their memory is bad sometimes turn out to be depressed still. As depressed people suffer from poor registration and concentration, they commonly complain of poor memory, whether they have had ECT or not.

Overall, ECT has had an extremely bad press. Some years ago a group of people handed out leaflets to psychiatrists going into a meeting at the Royal Society of Medicine in London. The leaflets referred to psychiatrists 'frying people's brains'. Such views are extreme. However, some of the American states have banned the use of ECT, indicating that the anti-ECT lobby has a lot of support there. It is likely that the abandonment of ECT in this country would have little overall effect. When we wrote the first edition of this book, we could still see a place for this treatment in our own practice. However, in the last ten years none of our patients has had it, and we now favour less drastic treatment that may work over a longer time span. Some psychiatrists still use ECT, particularly in older people with severe depression, and junior psychiatrists still have to be trained in its use.

Psychosurgery

In the past, this was used for certain psychiatric disorders. The commonest operation has been the **prefrontal leucotomy**, or **lobotomy** as it is sometimes called. The functions of the frontal part, or **lobe**, of the brain, which is just behind the forehead, are extremely subtle, and it is possible to do without this part of the brain, both physically and socially. It is partly concerned with emotional responses, and the idea behind prefrontal leucotomy was to cut through the nerve connections that were responsible for this function in order to lessen the intensity of mental suffering. The original operations were extremely crude, but nowadays radiation from radioactive needles placed in this part of the brain produces the same effect with much more precision. The radiation is very slight, and affects only the nerve cells very close to its source. The operation is very rarely carried out now, and only in centres that have special experience of it. The main side effects were a loss of creativity, an inability to learn new skills, and a degree of emotional coarsening, or 'flattening'.

We have always had very considerable worries about psychosurgery, centring mainly on a distaste for producing permanent changes in a person's brain. In addition, although psychosurgery did appear to benefit some people experiencing extreme suffering, it was never properly evaluated, so we have no conclusive information about the balance of benefits and drawbacks, or the exact indications for its use.

Under the 1983 Mental Health Act, psychosurgery cannot be carried out without the patient's consent and the independent opinion of three specially appointed people, one of whom must be a doctor, that the consent is valid. Neither of us has seen it used for more than twenty years, and it should probably now be consigned to history.

SOCIAL AND PSYCHOLOGICAL TREATMENTS

While patients are in hospital, and frequently after they return home, they will usually be offered some form of **social**, **psychosocial** or **psychological treatment**. This can involve organising **environmental features** in the most beneficial way, or individual treatment, or both. There are several ways of doing this, depending on the facilities available locally and also to some extent on the views of local clinical staff about the usefulness of a given facility for a particular individual.

As we described above, severe mental illness brings with it not only the obvious symptoms such as suicidal ideas, hallucinations and loss of touch with reality, but less obvious and more persistent ones which can cause equally resistant problems. Unlike a straightforward physical condition such as a broken leg or pneumonia, which people can observe and understand relatively easily, those suffering from severe mental illness usually look perfectly normal. This can make it hard for others, and indeed even for the sufferer, to appreciate the unseen difficulties that may persist. These less obvious problems centre on the **negative symptoms**, described on page 28, such as slowness, poor concentration, tiredness, underactivity, loss of confidence in one's abilities, loss of interest in previous hobbies or friends, and an inability to show one's feelings.

All this may add up to your relative not wanting, and not immediately being able, to return to a demanding career or a full family life and responsibilities. Social treatments are designed to help in overcoming these difficulties by providing a setting in which people can be gradually encouraged to return to a previous level of outside interest and function. It is important for all those concerned with the patient's well-being to appreciate the special and unforeseen problems that this transition can entail.

Occupational therapy (see also p. 80)

Most NHS hospitals have **occupational therapy (OT) departments**, and most community mental health teams will include an occupational therapist. OT offers a range of activities that will help people to regain lost interests, skills and concentration, while allowing them to feel that their time is creatively and usefully employed during the day. These activities may be organised on a ward, in day care centres or at home. Clients can find it very helpful to have a timetable or structure to their day, and to have somewhere to be apart from the ward or their home.

The activities offered may at first sight look, both to you and to your relative, much too simple and undemanding. But the fact is that it may be hard, indeed even quite a shock, to realise how poor his or her concentration or interest has become. The activities are, in fact, carefully **graded** to the individual's current capacity, with the aim of helping him or her to regain skills steadily and gradually, and to minimise the risk of failure—which can be very discouraging at this stage of recovery. People will usually be provided with more complex and demanding tasks, as they become capable of them. Sometimes the OT department will aim to foster totally new interests, such as pottery, art, crafts or cookery, which clients can continue to develop. Your encouragement can be very valuable here.

Many of the activities offered by OT departments centre on useful occupational or domestic skills that can be employed to get people back into the routine of looking after themselves.

These are particularly important if they have been ill for an appreciable period. Art and crafts are used to stimulate and to foster a sense of creative achievement; music, drama and dance may be useful in encouraging people to express themselves.

Tony was an intelligent man who had been admitted to hospital on account of a severe depression: he had little energy, and could hardly be bothered to do anything. His psychiatrist and occupational therapist together worked out a daily programme with him. This was designed so as to encourage him to use what concentration he could muster, but very little pressure was put on him. He had three sessions in the pottery department, where it was suggested that he should try his hand at making small, simple objects. Also, he helped with moving finished pottery around, and did other small tasks. Clearly the occupational therapist did not actually *need* his help, but in this way she kept him close by her for much of the time, talking to him, encouraging and organising him. When he returned to the ward, he enjoyed the small satisfaction of having done something constructive, however trifling. This was the first stage in a plan to help Tony regain confidence and interest, and as he got better he was gradually led into doing more.

Sheltered workshops

Mental health staff, and indeed clients themselves, may prefer a more **industrial setting** in which to re-establish confidence and concentration and to assist the return to work. Sheltered workshops tend to be used for people who have continuing problems. As with occupational therapy, it can be helpful just for the person to have a set timetable, and to have things to do and think about. Working alongside someone else can be beneficial, and actually working *with* someone more so. Again, the range of activities—packing or light industrial work—may look far too simple, but it is graded to the individual's capacity at the time. It may be that all someone can manage on a given day is to sit at his or her work place for half an hour.

Occupational and sheltered work used to signal the start of a return to full-time **employment**. But with current rates of unemployment the emphasis has now shifted to enabling patients to regain lost skills, or to learn new skills if their previous work record was poor. Sheltered work also provides a working environment where they can earn some money, get used to the routine of a job again and participate in interesting activities during the day. This may yet lead to a return to full employment, but it can also be an end in itself.

Patrick had suffered from a series of depressive illnesses and was also rather obsessive in his habits. This made him slow, if very sure, in any task he might undertake. Unfortunately, 'slow but sure' is not a quality suited to most jobs these days, and he never managed to stay in work for very long. Recent years had seen him unemployed for most of the time. This did not help his tendency to depression or his relationship with his ageing parents, with whom he lived.

Eventually, it was decided to offer him a place in a sheltered workshop. He tried out a number of tasks: the one that most suited him had become available only recently in the workshop, and consisted of entering statistical information on to computer discs. Patrick's slowness did not matter too much here, and his accuracy was appreciated. It didn't seem likely that he would ever work in open employment of this type, but he had his place in the workshop and was much more cheerful. His parents appreciated the fact that he was no longer moping around the house in the daytime, and family life was much easier. In Patrick's case, sheltered work played an important part in preventing an enduring and serious mental problem from getting worse, and helped him to continue to live in the community. Nowadays most sheltered workshops are run by charities, and may be linked with day care provided by social services. Local provision of these is therefore variable and there may not be easy access to one in your area.

Group meetings

Some mental health teams organise regular meetings between staff and patients, where patients' problems and experiences, both past and present, may be discussed. While some patients say that they find such meetings uncomfortable or boring, others find it very valuable to be able to talk to or listen to others who understand their problems and have shared some of the same experiences. Not all teams place the same emphasis on group meetings. In some, they may be regarded as a central part of treatment and attention will focus on events that happened to sufferers in their childhood, in the belief that these are of crucial importance to the development of their condition. This approach is likely to be referred to as **group therapy**. Groups in other settings, such as day care centres, may attend much more directly to everyday problems and how to solve them.

Individual treatments

Some clients will be offered time on their own with clinical staff to discuss their difficulties. As health professionals in the community now tend to work in teams, the staff member involved may be from any one of the variety of professions described on pp. 75–80. The sort of individual therapy offered can be extremely varied, from counselling about recent problems, or specific programmes designed to help modify particular difficulties, to detailed sessions in which the relationship between earlier experiences and current problems is explored.

Sometimes only a few sessions are offered; in other cases, weekly sessions over several months or a year or two. The sort of help to be provided should be negotiated and agreed between the client and the staff. This treatment can be a great help to some people by getting them to understand what has happened to them, how to prevent it happening again, and how to cope in the future, should similar problems recur.

The regular opportunity to talk privately with a member of the clinical staff is often referred to as 'individual psychotherapy', or just 'psychotherapy'. It takes a whole range of forms—sometimes also called 'the talking therapies'—and the procedure used by particular practitioners may reflect quite closely their adherence to a chosen theory of human psychology.

Psychoanalysis is a type of psychotherapy carried out along lines dictated by the beliefs of psychoanalytic theory. Psychoanalysts have always tended to form splinter groups, each with a different if related theory—so you get Freudian analysts, Jungian analysts, Kleinian analysts and so forth. But all share the opinion that earlier experiences determine later mental problems in a rather precise way.

As is well known, psychoanalysis started in central Europe, but it has been most influential in the United States, although its popularity there has waned. There are some well known British practitioners, but by and large British psychiatrists are rather suspicious of elaborate theories supported by what they consider to be doubtful evidence. They prefer to keep things relatively simple and will only take as facts what has been clearly established—although they are perhaps readier to accept biologically based ideas than psychological ones, probably as a consequence of their medical training. In psychological matters, they are more influenced by the rather different theories of their clinical psychologist colleagues.

Members of the public often don't realise this, and are rather surprised to find that psychiatrists are more concerned with current practical difficulties than with probing the recesses of the mind. While there is no doubt about the earlier influence of psychoanalytic ideas, and psychiatrists readily recognise that early experiences are likely to be important in shaping the way people behave in adult life, they tend to think that not a lot can be done to change what has already happened. Psychoanalysts, in contrast, think that very early bad experiences can affect later life by influencing it in ways that the individual does not know about, and that bringing these influences into consciousness can help to destroy them.

Most psychotherapy carried out in the National Health Service is 'supportive psychotherapy', concentrating on everyday problems, although with some attempt to give the patient insight into his or her behaviour. Clinical psychologists may offer psychotherapy of this type, and they may also provide 'behavioural psychotherapy' or the increasingly influential 'cognitive behavioural therapy' (CBT).

'Cognitive' means knowing or perceiving, and **cognitive therapy** is based on the idea that people's emotional states depend on their attitudes to what goes on around them. A depressed person is locked into a gloomy misinterpretation of events and of the light these cast on him or her—a pattern that has become automatic and therefore difficult to shift. The therapist points out these habitual attitudes to the patient, and helps the latter to monitor his or her style of thinking. Making the processes involved more apparent gives the client the chance of changing them into more appropriate and beneficial ones. This newer therapy is effective in treating depression and also helps to keep clients well once they have recovered, as they can themselves spot and deal with any tendency to slip back into old ways.

An exciting recent development has been to offer cognitive behavioural therapy not only for depression, but also for schizophrenia and manic depression: **CBT for psychosis**. It was thought for many years that, because delusional ideas are often held with great conviction, it was not possible to change them by rational argument. Thus 'talking therapies' were not offered to those with a psychosis, and treatment concentrated on medication and various social and family interventions. However, evidence is now accumulating that shows that by helping a sufferer to review the evidence for his or her beliefs, in a sympathetic and non-confrontational way, even very fixed ideas can change. This treatment is not generally available, but many clinicians are very interested in learning how to apply it to severe mental illnesses, and it may become more available in the future.

Another talking therapy, one that *is* increasingly available, is counselling. This is not a well defined term—it can cover a range of approaches from supportive listening to sophisticated help with dealing with particular difficulties. Counselling is usually short-term, and rarely offered to those with severe mental health problems, but it is increasingly available at GPs' surgeries and health centres, as well as privately. Although your relative *should* be able to obtain such support from his or her key worker, either of you might find it useful to have an outside person to offer you support.

Family sessions

This form of social treatment has developed since the 1970s. Whole families are asked to meet together with one, or sometimes two, professional staff to discuss areas of difficulty. This kind of therapy is appropriate if sufferers are in close contact with their family, since, if so, relatives are likely to continue to be involved in their care. Again, family meetings are offered by staff as individual circumstances dictate: they may be limited to one or two occasions, or continue over some months or years. Some families find it extremely useful to focus on how they get on together, to understand why difficulties have occurred in the past and to consider how they might help each other cope with problems. A particular kind of psychosocial family work has been developed, in both the UK and the USA, which deals with the problems routinely found when carers have to cope with mentally ill relatives. This kind of approach has been shown to be very effective in helping clients to remain well, and in helping carers to cope better with longstanding problems. This might be available from your local mental health team—you can ask for family help under the new Community Care Act.

Relatives' groups

Most relatives' groups are **self-help groups** organised by interested relatives to enable them to share problems and support each other. The **National Schizophrenia Fellowship**, the best-known of these organisations in the UK, is worth describing in some detail—you may find what it offers useful to you.

The NSF offers a variety of services to relatives, some of which are more or less restricted to those who become members of the organisation. Participation in local NSF groups provides information about local services but also, more importantly perhaps, personal support and exchange of information about caring problems. Membership also gives access to the various projects the local groups may have set up. These may include social events, holidays, housing, sheltered employment, social clubs and day centres. The group can also provide 'muscle' to back up individual members' dissatisfactions or complaints. In addition, there is the facility of being able to telephone knowledgeable NSF members in local areas, and a twenty-four-hour help line is now available.

NSF headquarters also offer an advisory service that is available to all. This supplies information and advice about housing, holidays, employment, benefits and other services provided by the statutory, voluntary and private sectors. There is also a library of video- and audio-tapes covering much of current expert opinion about schizophrenia. There are lists of publications helpful to relatives, some of which are produced by the Fellowship itself.

Advice is available about complaints procedures. Indeed, the NSF will take up specific problems with the statutory services if the individual's own attempts have been unsuccessful. This service is limited by the availability of personnel, and so may give priority to members. The sorts of problems that the NSF often has to deal with are, for instance, the threatened or actual discharge home of a still unwell patient to a relative who cannot cope, the refusal of hospital admission to a very sick person at home, lack of information about medication and its likely side effects, inadequate service from the family doctor, as well as general dissatisfaction with psychiatric services. The NSF also campaigns and lobbies on issues brought to their attention by relatives and carers, representing their views to policy makers and service providers such as commissioners, health authorities, local authorities, government and professional bodies.

The **Manic Depression Fellowship** is an organisation for those who suffer from manic depressive illness and their relatives. For a small annual fee it offers to members a quarterly newsletter, occasional fact sheets, meetings and, perhaps most especially, assistance in setting up local self-help groups. Compared with the NSF, a larger proportion of members are actual sufferers.

MIND's local associations sometimes can and do act as support groups for troubled relatives.

ALTERNATIVE MEDICINE AND PSYCHIATRY

You may come across other treatments for which claims are made, such as special **diets** and the use of **ionisers**. Distressed patients and their relatives may be dissatisfied with the response to routine therapy, particularly if it doesn't seem to improve things much, and they are sometimes willing to place their faith in something that appears to offer an alternative. Unfortunately, some of these treatments are proposed by uncritical enthusiasts, and others by people with a strong financial interest in promoting them.

Practitioners in this area are now organising themselves into societies that will establish standards of practice and methods of investigating the effectiveness of their treatment. Nevertheless, we have considerable reservations, and feel that relatives should be cautious about unconventional treatments of this sort. It will be more useful, in our view, if your dissatisfaction with the service your sick relative is getting leads you to press for better services of the conventional kind.

6 Legal Matters

The most important part of this chapter deals with the rules that have to be followed in arranging **compulsory admission** and **compulsory treatment**, and the safeguards that exist. Since we wrote the first edition of this book, the reduction in beds has made it harder to get admitted to hospital. As a result, people are often admitted in the later stages of a crisis and so a higher proportion of admissions are compulsory ones—around 30 per cent in the services we work in. Sadly, therefore, an appreciable number of our readers will require information about compulsory admission, so we will give it in some detail. Rather than summarise all the mental health legislation, we concentrate on those parts most likely to be relevant to people suffering from schizophrenia and manic depressive illness.

The rights of clients and relatives

Most admissions to hospital happen because clients agree with members of the mental health team that this is the best way to deal with their difficulties. This is known as **informal** or **voluntary admission**. Indeed, people are always given the opportunity to agree to admission when it is thought to be necessary. Sometimes, though, an individual may need to be admitted to, or detained in, hospital against his or her will. In Britain we have always been careful to defend the rights of individuals, and **compulsory admission** is a legal process with legal safeguards. The law in England and Wales was revised by the **1983 Mental Health Act**, under which the nearest relative of a compulsorily detained client has both rights and duties, and may be involved in the admission procedure. Acts along similar lines apply in Scotland and Northern Ireland.

The rights of voluntary clients

Voluntary admission to hospital is by mutual agreement of the client and of the clinical team. Under these circumstances, clients have the right to refuse treatment and to discharge themselves. Clearly, though, if an individual refuses to comply with the recommended treatment plan, the alliance between client and team is undermined. He or she must therefore weigh carefully the pros and cons of downright refusal of treatment and those of discharge against medical advice. It is much better to try to discuss the problems with staff in order to find a mutually acceptable solution. In extreme cases, the team may decide to discharge the client if he or she is not cooperating with plans for treatment, on the grounds that care in hospital has ceased to be of benefit. Even in such cases they should offer some kind of alternative provision, particularly where the patient is clearly suffering from the consequences of a severe mental condition such as schizophrenia or manic depressive illness.

If clients do decide that they want to discharge themselves against medical advice, they may be asked to sign a statement to that effect. This might be used in the light of subsequent developments to protect the clinical team from allegations of negligence.

If people who are seriously disturbed and a potential danger to themselves or others agree to be admitted on a voluntary basis, and then change their minds and want to discharge themselves, the medical team may well decide that they must remain in the hospital on a compulsory basis. Similarly, if someone deteriorates in hospital despite the attentions of staff, the team may consider compulsory detention, particularly if the sufferer is refusing a needed treatment. This state of affairs does give considerable powers to psychiatrists, which you and your relative may feel uneasy about. In most cases these powers are used for the genuine benefit of the client, and there are safeguards, which we describe on p. 129.

The client's nearest relative

The nearest relative is the one the client usually lived with or who was most involved in caring for him or her before admission to hospital. Where there is more than one such person or the client lives alone, the **legal nearest relative** is the one closest to the top of the list in Table 12.

TABLE 12
Nearest relatives

husband/wife
son/daughter
father/mother
brother/sister
grandparent
grandchild
uncle/aunt
nephew/niece

A cohabitee may qualify as the nearest relative if he or she has lived with the client for at least six months as husband or wife. He or she does not, however, take over the rights of the actual husband or wife unless there has been a legal separation or divorce. A person other than a relative who has lived with the client for at least five years counts as a relative, but in the last position on the list.

Who can be admitted or detained against their will?

Compulsory procedures can only be used to admit or detain clients suffering from certain types of disorder, the rules governing which are laid down in the 1983 Act. An individual must be suffering from a **mental disorder** sufficiently severe to make admission appropriate, and must have **refused** voluntary admission. The admission must be in the interests of the client's own health or safety, or for the protection of others.

'Mental disorder' covers three conditions: mental illness, psychopathic disorder and mental impairment (learning disability). (It **excludes** sexual deviation and dependence on alcohol or drugs.) Slightly different powers apply to each of these three conditions. Those suffering from 'mental illness' are subject to the widest powers; except for the Northern Irish one, the British Acts do not define what is meant by this term, but it clearly covers both schizophrenia and manic depressive illness. Compulsory admission is most commonly used for suicidal clients, for those who act on beliefs of persecution, and for those who are incapable of looking after themselves physically or who may cause themselves untold social damage, such as running up huge debts.

Admission and detention under the Mental Health Act 1983
Different **Sections** of the Act describe the proper procedures for use in particular circumstances. The duration of detention varies according to the procedure used, and the recommendation for detention can be renewed when it runs out. There are particular rules for clients admitted following criminal proceedings, but those are not discussed here.

Under **Section 136** of the Act, people suspected of being a danger to themselves or others and found in a public place can be taken to a 'place of safety' by a **police officer**. These powers are used with increasing frequency, but are usually monitored by a committee that includes representatives from the police and the local mental health Trust. Usually, a place of safety means a hospital, making it relatively easy for the client to be assessed by a doctor and an approved social worker. This must be done within seventy-two hours. A 'place of safety' can also mean a residential home or a police station, but these are less suitable and less commonly used.

Under **Section 135**, an approved social worker can apply to a magistrate to issue a warrant for premises to be searched for someone suspected of being mentally disordered. There must be grounds for believing that he or she is being mistreated or neglected, or is alone and unable to care for him- or herself. The warrant is carried out by a police officer, accompanied by a social worker and a doctor.

However, these circumstances are relatively unusual. A commoner situation arises when, because of a disturbance indoors—at home or elsewhere—someone calls the **family doctor**, who decides that the sufferer should be admitted but cannot persuade him or her to enter hospital voluntarily. The procedure then requires an **application**, which can be signed either by a specially approved social worker or by the nearest relative. There also has to be one or more **medical recommendations**. If there is only one such recommendation, this permits an **emergency admission**, under **Section 4** of the Act. In this case the medical recommendation should preferably be from a doctor who knows the person, most usually his or her GP. The client can be held for only seventy-two hours, unless another doctor is obtained within this period to make an additional recommendation, thus converting it into a Section 2 admission (see below). A social worker signing the application form without the knowledge of the nearest relative must, with all urgency, tell the relative what has happened. Both the doctor and the social worker must have seen the client within twenty-four hours of signing their part of the Section. Thus the decision to 'section' is based primarily on how the person is on that particular day, and previous problems, however worrying, if they are not current, do not always get taken into consideration.

Admission for assessment requires the recommendation of *two* doctors, one of whom must be recognised as having special psychiatric expertise. This type of admission is permitted by **Section 2** of the Act, and the compulsory power lasts for twenty-eight days. The guidelines to the Act make it clear that Section 2 permits compulsory treatment by physical methods such as drugs or ECT.

Clients who have been admitted compulsorily can be stopped from leaving the hospital by staff, and if they do leave they can be brought back. The nature of this provision has been changed in the Mental Health (Patients in the Community) Act of 1995. Patients on these Sections, and on some other Sections imposed by courts, can now be brought back at any time within six months or, if this is later, the end of the existing authority for detention. If they are *not* brought back within this period, this power is lost.

Although people can be treated under Section 2, **Section 3** of the Act refers specifically to **admission for treatment**. The power to detain lasts for up to six months, but can then be renewed for a further six months. After that it can be renewed annually. Under Section 3, if the nearest relative objects, the social worker cannot make the application. However, if the social worker thinks the relative is being unreasonable, he or she may apply to a County Court for the nearest relative's function to be transferred to someone else, who need not be another relative. The guidelines to the 1983 Act emphasise that where a patient is known to the mental health team, Section 3 is more appropriate than Section 2.

There may be circumstances in which you feel your relative needs compulsory admission. One way of doing this is to call the family doctor, and to sign the application yourself. Another way is to ask the local social services department to arrange for an approved social worker to consider the case. If satisfied that compulsory admission cannot be avoided, the social worker will then make an application under the Act. If he or she does *not* think compulsory admission is justified, he or she must inform you in writing. The social worker is also obliged to consider all other alternatives to compulsory admission.

There are also powers under **Section 5** of the Act that can be used by designated doctors and nurses to prevent a client from leaving, even when he or she originally agreed to go into hospital voluntarily. Once more, it must be thought that the client is a danger to him- or herself or to others. This power to detain is important, because otherwise the client would have to be allowed to leave, and might experience considerable suffering or damage before the procedures of Section 4 could be arranged.

Details of the Sections of the 1983 Mental Health Act that govern compulsory admission procedures are summarised in Table 13.

Safeguards following a compulsory admission

It is possible for the compulsory powers to be revoked before they run out, and indeed this is the commonest outcome for Section 3. This is usually done by the doctor in charge of the client, the 'Responsible Medical Officer' (RMO). For instance, the doctor may revoke an emergency Section (Section 4), feeling that, although it was a reasonable course of action at the time, it now looks to have been inappropriately applied. In another case, the client may have asked for the compulsory order to be suspended. He or she may be considerably better and, in any event, likely to be reasonably cooperative with treatment, either as an informal in-patient or as an out-patient. The original requirements for the Section now no longer apply. In such cases, the doctor will often be happy to agree, feeling that treatment by mutual consent is more pleasant and more likely to be effective.

The **hospital managers** can also revoke compulsory powers. These people have nothing to do with the management of the hospital: they are lay people, and the panel may include non-executive directors of the **hospital trust** and coopted or associate members. Clients can appeal directly to the hospital managers to discharge them, and do not need anyone's permission to do so. A managers' hearing will then be arranged, and the panel may confirm the client's discharge. Clients may ask for a solicitor to represent them.

If a client is discharged from compulsory detention, the nearest

TABLE 13

1983 Mental Health Act Part II: compulsory admission

Section	Purpose	Applicant	Medical recommendation	Duration	Outcome
4	Emergency asssessment (mental disorder)	Nearest relative or approved social worker, who must have seen the patient within the previous 24 hours	Any doctor	72 hours	Discharge or order: by lapse, by consultant, by managers, by nearest relative. Conversion to Section 2 by second medical recommendation
2	Assessment (Mental disorder)	Nearest relative or approved social worker, who must attempt to inform the nearest relative	Two doctors, one approved under the Mental Health Act as having special expertise in psychiatry	28 days	Discharge of order: by lapse, by consultant, by managers, by nearest relative. by MHRT Conversion to Section 3
3	Treatment (i) Mental illness or severe mental impairment (ii) Psychopathic disorder or mental impairment if treatable	Nearest relative or approved social worker, provided that she has attempted to consult the nearest relative, who must consent	Two doctors, as above, giving reasons for detention, form of disorder and consideration of other methods of dealing with the patient	6 months, renewable for a further 6 months, then at yearly intervals	Discharge of order: by lapse, by consultant, by managers, by nearest relative, by MHRT

relative must be informed, unless either that person or the client has requested otherwise.

Clients also have the right to appear before a **Mental Health Review Tribunal (MHRT)**, which may order their release. The hospital managers have a duty to inform compulsorily detained clients about their rights and, in particular, about their right of appeal to these tribunals. Provided the client agrees, the managers must also inform the nearest relative of these rights, and in certain cases the relative can apply to the tribunal for the client to be reviewed. The application must be in writing. Clients can ask to be **represented** at the tribunal by a friend or relative, or by a legal representative. MIND (see Appendix 2) offers help with representation. Legal aid is available to all who appeal to the MHRT, and the representation organised by MIND is also free.

These tribunals are independent bodies that ensure that people admitted to hospital are not being kept there unnecessarily. Each National Health Executive in England has one, and there is one for the whole of Wales. (For the procedures in Scotland and Northern Ireland see p. 137.) The hearings are conducted by a **president**, who is a lawyer, with one medical and one lay colleague to help. The main duty of the tribunals is to decide whether a person can be released from hospital; they can also order them to be discharged at some future date. They can compel witnesses to attend, and take evidence under oath. Hearings are usually in private, although the client or relative can request a public hearing.

Clients are allowed to apply to tribunals only at certain intervals. At you might suspect, there is no right of appeal to the tribunal where detention is compelled under those Sections of the Act, such as Section 4, that hold for only seventy-two hours. Details are given in Tables 14 and 15.

The right of patients to appeal both to the hospital managers and to a Mental Health Review Tribunal has sometimes led to a duplication of procedures, and there are currently plans to remove the duty of hospital managers to hear appeals.

If you are the nearest relative, you can discharge an individual held under the powers of the Mental Health Act. This requires seventy-two hours' notice in writing to the hospital managers, so the power doesn't apply to those Sections of the Act that empower detention for only seventy-two hours. The medical officer in

TABLE 14

Periods of eligibility for Mental Health Review Tribunals

Mental Health Act 1983	First 14 days	First 6 months	Second 6 months	Annually
Sections 4, 5, 136 (72 hours)	—	—	—	—
Section 2 (28 days)	✓	—	—	—
Section 3 (treatment order)	—	✓	✓	✓
Section 37 (hospital order)	—	—	✓	✓
Sections 37 and 41 (hospital order with restriction order)	—	—	✓	✓

TABLE 15
Automatic Mental Health Review Tribunals

Mental Health Act 1983	First 6 months	Second 6 months	Every 3 years
Section 3 (treatment order)	—	✓	✓
Section 37 (hospital order)	—	—	✓
Sections 37 and 41 (hospital order with restriction order)	—	—	✓

charge of treatment can countermand your powers of discharge, but this in turn must be done in writing and you can then refer your relative to a Mental Health Review Tribunal, provided she is not detained under Section 2.

MIND's legal department will always advise you, and the organisation's booklet *A Mental Health Review Tribunal May Help You* explains how to apply. You should be able to get this from your hospital social worker, the local Community Health Council or the Citizens' Advice Bureau, or through MIND itself.

Compulsory treatment

In some emergency situations, any client can be given medication under common law without his or her consent, although the treatment given must be appropriate to the scale of the emergency. Indeed, this is actually spelt out by the Mental Health Act for compulsorily detained clients. In other situations, voluntary clients can be treated only if they agree to it: they have the right to refuse under common law. Legal consent to treatment does not just mean the client agreeing to it. The doctor must explain the nature, purpose and effect of the treatment and the client must be of sound enough mind to understand it. However, there is no formal procedure for obtaining a voluntary client's consent to drug treatment—if he or she accepts the doctor's prescription, it is assumed that this indicates consent. ECT is regarded as the equivalent of a minor operation, and so clients are required to sign a consent form (see p. 112). If a voluntary client is so mentally disturbed that he or she cannot understand the nature of the treatment offered, the doctor is really obliged to convert the admission into a compulsory one.

Clients who are compulsorily detained are often able to consent to treatment in the normal way, but they can also, in certain circumstances, be treated against their will. However, **ECT** and **long-lasting courses of medicine** can be given only with the client's consent or on the strength of an **independent second medical opinion**—that is, the opinion of a doctor who does not work in the same hospital as the consultant responsible.

Any client can withdraw consent to treatment at any time. The psychiatrist's decision to embark on compulsory treatment of a detained client is then governed by the safeguards of the Mental Health Act. The cases of clients who are being treated compulsorily are monitored by the **Mental Health Act Commission** set up under the 1983 Act. This is an independent body made up of legal and medical professionals and lay people, and responsible to the Secretary of State for Health. Every three months, treatment must be reviewed with the client. If he or she can and does give consent to the proposed continuing treatment, the RMO has to sign a form to that effect. Otherwise, the case has to be reviewed by a second-opinion doctor provided by the Mental Health Act Commission, and only if he or she agrees can treatment proceed.

Members of the Commission also visit hospitals at least once or twice a year, and ensure the correct working of the 1983 Mental Health Act. If, at the time a detention order is due for renewal, treatment has had to be authorised by a second-opinion doctor, the doctor in charge of the client's case must report to the Commission on his or her condition and the progress of treatment. The Commission may itself request such a report at any time, and has the power to withdraw the authority for compulsory treatment, although it cannot discharge patients from detention.

In April 1996 an addition was made to the legal powers of psychiatrists brought in under the Mental Health (Patients in the Community) Act. This allows for **supervised discharge** of certain people detained in hospital—most often those detained under Section 3—under the 1983 Mental Health Act. The introduction of this legislation has been accompanied by a lot of public debate in response to concerns about people who do not do well after discharge from hospital because they habitually omit to take medication, thus making it impossible to maintain their care in the community. On the other hand, some think that these powers detract too much from the civil liberties of people with severe mental illness. It is a matter, as with all this legislation, of balancing the right to treatment of people whose mental state prevents cooperation against their right to refuse.

Supervised discharge applies to people who do not need care in hospital any longer, but who present a substantial risk of serious harm to their own health or safety, or to the safety of others, unless their aftercare is supervised. A supervisor, usually the key worker, is appointed, who has the power to require his or her client to reside in a specified place and to attend for medical treatment and rehabilitation, and to convey the client to wherever he or she is to attend for occupation, education or treatment. If the arrangement fails, the care team has to review the care plan. At the review the team should consider whether compulsory admission under the 1983 Act is necessary. Clients cannot be given medical treatment *in the community* against their will. Supervised discharge initially lasts six months, but can be extended.

The application for supervised discharge is made by the RMO while the client is still in hospital under a Section, and should be accompanied by a medical recommendation and a recommendation from an approved social worker.

At the time of writing, we do not yet know if this power will add significantly to the benefit of clients living at home. Psychiatrists may be reluctant to apply it in case bad feeling results and interferes with effective long-term care.

Clients' mail

Except for clients in 'special hospitals' like Broadmoor, mail **from** a client cannot be intercepted unless the person to whom it is addressed has asked for this **in writing**. The client has to be informed of the interception by the hospital authorities, again in writing. Mail **to** a client in an ordinary psychiatric hospital cannot be intercepted.

Complaining about treatment or the use of compulsory powers

You or your relative may complain, either during admission or later, about any aspect of care. In addition to the normal channels open to the citizen (such as writing to Members of Parliament, Ministers of the Crown, the Parliamentary Commissioner, the Health Service Commissioner or the local community health centre), there are **three** special sources of redress for clients and their relatives.

The hospital managers should be approached first, and only if you are still not satisfied should you take things further. Secondly, you can approach the Mental Health Review Tribunals, already mentioned on p. 131. Thirdly, relatives and clients may apply to the Mental Health Act Commission, either by letter, or when its members are visiting the hospital. The Commission may deal with a complaint directly, or under certain circumstances by referring it to other procedures set up for the purpose. Clients and relatives can contact the Commission only about procedures that come within the powers of the Mental Health Act—basically, compulsory admission and treatment. Other complaints should be dealt with through the hospital complaints procedure.

In Scotland and Northern Ireland, the procedures covering compulsory admission and treatment are laid down in separate Acts of Parliament. These are similar in principle to, but differ in detail from, the Mental Health Act that applies in England and Wales. If you live in Scotland or Northern Ireland you may obtain guidance about the local legislation from local branches of MIND, or from the hospital to which your relative has been admitted.

In Scotland, applications for compulsory admission must be submitted to a sheriff. There are no Mental Health Review Tribunals, but the Scottish equivalent of the Mental Health Act Commission, called the Mental Welfare Commission, has responsibility for reviewing and, if appropriate, discharging compulsory clients. It also looks after the interests of voluntary clients.

The Mental Health Act Commission for Northern Ireland also has the duty of reviewing the care and treatment of all mentally disordered people. However, it cannot discharge them. This can be done only by the Northern Ireland Mental Health Review Tribunal.

Finally, detained clients can **sue** for compensation, if the motive for detaining them was improper, or if the doctors were negligent in making their medical recommendations. They can sue anyone involved in the process—doctors, social workers, nurses, or indeed the nearest relative. However, they need the permission of the High Court to bring a civil action, and of the Director of Public Prosecutions to bring a criminal action.

Wills and contracts

As everyone knows, wills always start off with references to the person making the will as 'being of sound mind'. In fact, he or she has only to be of sound enough mind to know what his or her will means. People must know what property they have, who, if anyone, has a claim on it, and what the relative strengths of their claims are. The will must be legible and unambiguous. Solicitors may seek medical opinion on their clients' state of mind.

Contracts require a sound mind in the same way that wills do. Marriage, being a contract, would in theory be void if one of the partners was at the time incapable of understanding the nature and responsibilities of marriage. More usually marriages are regarded as voidable, or annullable, not because a partner was incapable of giving consent, but because he or she was suffering at the time from a mental disorder of such a nature and extent as to unfit him or her for marriage. In practice, this procedure is rarely used.

Other rights and duties

For most people admission to hospital is temporary, and they can **vote** as from their home address. For clients staying longer, a general hospital or nursing home can be used as an address for the purposes of the electoral roll. However, a mental hospital is *not* a valid address. Compulsory clients who do not have a place of residence outside the hospital cannot vote.

People seeing a doctor for treatment of a mental illness are excused **jury service**.

If individuals become aware of any disability that is likely to affect their ability to **drive**, they are obliged to inform the Driver and Vehicle Licensing Agency. Mental illness is such a disability, although the exact conditions that qualify as disability are not stipulated. Clearly, people who are acutely ill with schizophrenia or manic depressive disorder should not drive. Fortunately, they do not usually attempt to. Problems are more likely to occur if your relative is recovering: you may not be sure whether it is a good idea for him or her to drive, particularly if he or she is taking medication. Most psychiatric medication interferes to some extent with the ability to drive. There are now (from March 1996) clear guidelines concerning the right to drive for people with schizophrenia or manic depressive illness. Following an acute episode of schizophrenia requiring hospital admission, an individual must not drive a car or motorbike for six months, and the licence will be restored only when he or she has been free from acute symptoms during this period and if he or she is fully compliant with any medication prescribed. A licence is given for only one, two or three years, and the patient is subject to medical review when he or she needs to renew it. Similar rules apply to people with manic depressive disorder, and if they have frequent attacks the period in which they cannot drive may be increased to twelve months. These disorders virtually exclude sufferers from driving heavy goods vehicles, as might be imagined. Interestingly, the Driver and Vehicle Licensing Agency do not consider the medication given to people for these conditions as excluding them from driving.

It may be useful to talk to your relative's doctor about the question of driving. In an extreme case, if you cannot persuade your relative not to drive, you yourself may have to contact the DVLA. The doctor may have to do this, anyway, if he or she feels that public duty overrides the duty of professional confidentiality.

The responsibility for written information about rights under the Mental Health Act rests with the hospital managers, via their authorised agents in the hospital, so the hospital will have leaflets about these matters. Other organisations you may find useful, such as the NSF and MIND, can be found in Appendix 2.

7 Looking After Yourself

Your own welfare may not seem an obvious aspect for you to be concerned about—and it is easily overlooked. The focus may be so much on your relative, mentally ill and vulnerable, that your own feelings or problems are forgotten or not recognised. This is a great pity, and indeed one of the reasons for this book.

Living and coping with an individual who has, or has had, a severe mental illness can be rewarding, with no particular problems. Often, however, this is not the case, especially at first, and your own reactions may be crucial to your ability to deal with problems effectively and to prevent crises from developing. Individuals with some severe mental illnesses, particularly schizophrenia, can be especially sensitive to the **family atmosphere**. If you are able to cope effectively with the difficulties that arise, tension will be reduced and arguments avoided.

The first important thing to be learned is that it is in everyone's interest for you to try to deal with difficulties **calmly** and **with tolerance**, even if you aren't feeling particularly calm or tolerant. This helps sufferers to recover more quickly and, indeed, keeps them well.

For example, a woman who was living with her twin sister, who had become ill, described how initially she had been very impatient and irritated by her behaviour, particularly her inability to do certain things or help around the house. As time passed, however, she realised that this attitude was making things worse. 'I realised it was no good,' she said, 'so I learned to be more patient.' This came about without anyone's advice or help—she just became aware with the passage of time that some things were helpful, and others made life harder. This more patient and tolerant attitude, expecting a little less and not becoming so angry, made the atmosphere much calmer between them, and helped her sister to recover faster from the illness.

The second important principle that will help you to cope is the need to have **your own interests** and continue to lead **your own life** if you wish to. It is quite possible to be extremely caring and supportive while maintaining your own outside interests, going to work and going on holiday. All the same, people very often feel that they should give all of this up. But although it is quite natural to feel that you should not leave your ill relative alone at home in order to go out and enjoy yourself, this does seem to be a mistake. Those who are able to some extent to lead their own lives and who do not become totally immersed in looking after their relatives do feel better themselves, but also, very crucially, they thereby allow the sufferer some independence. From our observation, people who have lived with the mentally ill for many years very rarely have a holiday. But if they do start going out sometimes, or doing other things by themselves and for themselves—perhaps going to work, even, if only part-time—this can restore the balance and reduce the tendency to do too much for the other person, rather than **just enough**.

One couple were very worried that, if they left their son alone in the house for any length of time, he would set fire to the kitchen while making himself a cup of tea. In fact this had nearly happened on several occasions in the past, so it was not an unrealistic fear. However, after safeguarding the kitchen as much as possible beforehand, they tried a few hours away from home. No disaster happened, and it was possible to build on this in an attempt to restore some of this couple's own life and enjoyment together.

An issue related to the necessity of doing things for *your* satisfaction, and in the process allowing your relative some independence, is the danger of being too protective. People with severe mental illness are usually adults, even if they have not all managed to achieve much independent adult life, and it can be too easy for carers to get into the habit of doing and organising all the things that need to be done; to go back to treating them as children, unable to be left alone, to look after themselves or to make their own decisions. It is quite true that, at various stages in the course of severe mental health problems, people may lose the ability to look after themselves properly, or lose contact with reality and not care about such things. However, this state is not normally permanent.

In one family, Carl was able to cook a meal and do some cleaning and shopping, but it was easier and more efficient for his seventy-year-old mother to do it all for both of them. It took some time and effort to establish that Carl should do more than he did around the house, and to decide that he should be responsible for at least one meal a week. But once this was achieved it was possible to build on it, so that Carl felt that he had achieved something and was of some use at home, and his mother could be relieved of some of the responsibilities that she had always taken on alone.

The third important principle in coping with mental illness in the family is to avoid being too **intrusive**. While it is not a good idea to leave your ill relative totally alone and isolated—particularly as these illnesses have in any case a tendency to make the sufferer withdraw from other people—it is also useful to know when to leave him or her alone. 'I follow him around the house,' one mother said, 'I'm so worried what he'll do next.' While it is understandable and natural to worry, and while it may be necessary at times of acute illness to be very observant when there is a risk of suicide, this degree of worry, anger or upset runs the risk of continuing even when the illness is a little better. At this stage it can be very wearing for you—and quite destructive, if you have no relief. It may also prevent you developing more tolerant and realistic attitudes. It is often desirable for sufferers to be able to go and lie down in their own room for a while, as they may be oversensitive to the presence of other people and feel that they simply have to be left alone sometimes. One mother said, 'I know he gets upset at times and goes to his bedroom. I don't go in for a while, I just leave him. Then later on I'll offer him a cup of tea, take it in to him if he won't come down, and ask if things are any better.' A wife whose husband's inactivity made her very angry, as she had to take on all the household chores and child care as well as a part-time job, said, 'Sometimes I just go for a walk round the park to get away from him for a while. It means I can calm down and feel better when I go back in.'

Those who cope successfully with a relative with a mental health problem have usually come to recognise both what is helpful and what is not. It often happens that the expectations of a sufferer's future performance or lifestyle have to change. It can be tragic to watch a much loved son or daughter fall short of early hopes, or to see a partner not able to match the initial promise of a relationship. Many parents and spouses talk of a time similar to that following bereavement, and equally painful, when these adjustments take place in their hopes and expectations. It helps to be tactful about sharing these feelings with the sufferer.

Particularly if you are a partner, you are likely at one time or another to feel that you want to end the relationship. This is being realistic, and probably happens to every couple at some stage. In some cases it is the best outcome: sufferers and their families manage better with less frequent and less intense contact, particularly if this has been very upsetting in the past. Professionals often suggest that grown-up children who have been in hospital on account of mental illness should perhaps not return home to live full-time with their parents but go to live in a hostel, in sheltered housing or in their own flat. It may be a better and much more realistic long-term solution to maintain a degree of contact of your own choosing with a mentally ill individual living elsewhere, than to be forced to continue to live together when problems are insurmountable. Such decisions should only be made after discussion between you, your relative and his or her key worker.

For some people, the only compensation for caring for their relative comes from a sense of duty done. While this deserves respect, it should not blind them to what may be best for the individual concerned if, for example, home circumstances are so fraught that a separation would be the best answer. Those who feel that caring brings few rewards should try to make sure that other aspects of their lives compensate. One relative wisely advises, 'In order to cope with sometimes unbearable strain, you must keep well, eat well, and get as much sleep and exercise as you can. Try to keep up with your work and hobbies, and try to find support in what you can—religion, friendship, a sense of mission. Do not hide your difficulties from relatives and friends: if you do, they will think you do not need their sympathy.'

Holidays

Holidays can be a very important source of relief for those living with someone suffering from a mental illness. After all, it can be a full-time job, and other workers are entitled to periods of leave. Separate holidays are the ideal, at least on occasion, and you shouldn't feel guilty about this—it also gives your relative a break from you!

Some social services departments will organise holidays for the mentally ill, and you may find out about other possibilities from the Psychiatric Rehabilitation Association or the Holiday Care Service (see Appendix 2). Your relative may lack the energy or motivation to do this, so you may have to arrange the holiday for him or her. It may be possible to get financial help if you are both on a low income.

You may feel it is difficult to go off on holiday on your own. Sometimes, this feeling may be misplaced: your relative might well be able, and indeed happy, to manage alone for a week or two. In other circumstances, it may be realistic for you to feel that he or she couldn't manage. In this case, you might be able to persuade another relative either to come and stay, or to have him or her to stay while you are on holiday. You may need to make it clear that it is not a permanent arrangement! In some cases, your relative's mental health team may be sympathetic and arrange, say, a fortnight's respite care so that you can go on holiday—after all, to support someone undertaking much of the responsibility for caring for a mentally ill person is a very efficient use of services. In some areas local charities such as the NSF provide this facility, and the local social services department is also likely to be able to help.

The future

You may be able to retain an optimistic attitude to the future, to view things calmly and deal with problems as they arise. On the other hand, you may well feel pessimistic, see no way of changing things and expect grave and insoluble problems to persist. These attitudes tend to be self-fulfilling.

If your relative can accept treatment from clinical staff, if you encourage this and remain calm in crises, and if there are few additional problems such as financial hardship, an initially fraught situation may eventually become acceptable, routine and even quite satisfying. Then you may worry about becoming older: 'What will happen when I'm gone?' This is often a realistic fear, as many caring relatives, particularly parents, provide such high levels of support that they cannot be replaced. Ideally, part of the care that you provide should aim to enable your relative to become as independent as possible, like any other adult. Keeping up links with other family members and friends may be important for you, and also ensures that he or she has others to turn to at times. It is also sensible to make sure domestic skills are not lost, or the ability to look after him- or herself. Help with this is often provided by community occupational therapists who may visit your home, and your relative should be encouraged to take advantage of it.

It is important to remember that in time most people either recover from their illness or become adapted to its effects. Individuals may learn what can upset them and begin to avoid such triggers or in other ways reduce their effects. With sympathetic care, they may come to accept that medication has a useful role to play in the control of their illness and to comply with a dosage that has the fewest possible side effects. Many people will recover completely. Others will eventually be able to reduce or stop medication altogether. In time, your relative and you will probably become adept at recognising the warning signs of an impending relapse and obtain prompt treatment for it, thus reducing the length and upset of later bouts of illness. Many individuals and their carers are also able to say that such illnesses provide experiences that others can never have and that have added to their lives in unexpectedly fulfilling ways.

Getting further advice and information

We have mentioned many of these sources of support already. Information about your local NHS facilities may be available from your family doctor, although it must be said that some are less well informed than they might be. The mental health team dealing with your relative is perhaps a more reliable source; the team's linked social worker, or the 'duty social worker' at the local social services department, might be the best person to contact. One way of finding out about the available facilities is to ask at a discharge planning meeting or at a Care Programme Approach Review.

Other agencies that provide information about local facilities include the Citizens' Advice Bureau, the Community Health Council and your local branch of MIND.

Information about employment for the mentally ill can be obtained from the Disablement Resettlement Officer at your local Job Centre, who will also know about facilities for employment rehabilitation.

The National Schizophrenia Fellowship, set up by relatives of people with this condition, can be a great source of support as well as of information (see p. 167), as can SANE (p. 172). MIND (the National Association for Mental Health) are very good at meeting requests for information, and have a range of booklets on particular topics. The Mental Health Foundation, who commissioned the first edition of this book, also put out booklets and publications concerning related subjects. Several books give information about financial benefits, including the *Disability Rights Handbook* of the Disability Alliance Educational and Research Association, and the *National Welfare Benefits Handbook* and *Rights Guide to non-Means-Tested Social Security Benefits* published by the Child Poverty Action Group.

The names and addresses of over ten thousand self-help and community organisations in the United Kingdom, both national and local, are published by the Mental Health Foundation in their ***Someone to Talk to Directory***, available through your local library. It might be worth your while to look at this. More general reading you might consider includes the excellent *Understanding Mental Health* by Angelina Gibbs, published by the Consumers' Association, and *First Aid in Mental Health* by Joy Melville, published as an Unwin paperback. These books cover a wide variety of aspects of mental health, mostly from the viewpoint of the client.

The National Schizophrenia Fellowship have published a number of books that give a very clear view of the problems of living with someone suffering from schizophrenia. These include *Schizophrenia at Home*, *Living with Schizophrenia—by the Relatives*, and the harrowing *A Tragedy of Schizophrenia: the Wife's Tale*. Finally, the Office of Health Economics have published a booklet entitled *Schizophrenia*.

Appendix 1
Getting around the Benefit System

Benefits for people with mental illness are very complicated, and your relative's entitlements may not be at all clear. Benefits can be applied for directly at your local social security (DSS) office, or you can send off forms available there or at Post Offices.

Benefits and the entitlement to them are always changing, so it is best to seek out the most up-to-date advice. At the time of writing, you and your relative may have access to the following benefits.

Incapacity Benefit replaced the old Sickness and Invalidity Benefits in April 1995. It is based on National Insurance contributions and is not means-tested. This means that it is available to people with savings as well as to those without, and to those whose partners work full-time. In fact, within limits, mentally ill people can work while receiving Incapacity Benefit. Provided they receive no more than expenses, they may work in a voluntary capacity for up to sixteen hours a week. They may also work where the work is part of their treatment programme—for instance, in a sheltered workshop. However, they may not earn more than £44 a week. At or below this level the amount of benefit will not be affected. The rules governing the eligibility for Incapacity Benefit are more complicated than were those for the benefits they replace.

In certain circumstances, Incapacity Benefit can be topped up by Income Support. The rates of payment (as you might guess) are less generous than those of the old Invalidity Benefit, varying according to how long the individual has been out of work. The longer a person claims, the more money he or she will receive. However, this will cut into any Income Support.

Severe Disablement Allowance can be claimed by people incapable of work for at least twenty-eight weeks. This allowance is not based on National Insurance contributions, nor is it means-tested. People are entitled to Severe Disablement Allowance if their incapacity began on, or before, their twentieth birthday, or they have been assessed as being 75 per cent disabled by a Benefits Agency doctor, or they receive certain Disability Living Allowance (DLA) rates. The rules for working are the same as for Incapacity Benefit. Income Support can be used to top up the payment, and should always be claimed. This is particularly so where someone has been in receipt of Severe Disablement Allowance for more than a year. Again, Severe Disablement Allowance can be claimed even if the recipient's partner is working, or gets a pension, or has sizeable savings. Because it is based on disability and not on National Insurance contributions, it is available to people who have been unable to work for many years, or who have never worked. It is particularly useful for people who have developed severe mental illness under the age of twenty, and it also has advantages for those who are frequently admitted to hospital.

Income Support is not based on National Insurance contributions, but is means-tested. In order to be entitled, you have to have less than £8,000 in savings. Moreover, neither you nor your partner can be working for more than sixteen hours a week. Any savings over £3,000 cause a reduction in the amount of Income Support payable, which is calculated by the Department of Social Security according to a formula laid down by law that covers how much a particular person needs to live on each week. Sometimes the Benefits Agency makes mistakes in these calculations, so it is always worth getting someone to check them (see p. 153). Income Support is used to top up other benefits for those on low earnings, to ensure that an individual couple or family does not fall below the legal minimum. According to your circumstances, you may have the right to additional funds: up to nine different types of Income Support premium are available! These include the Disability Premium and the Carer's Premium. As might be imagined, the calculation of Income Support is very complicated and it pays to be guided through them by an expert.

Disability Living Allowance (DLA) is for those who need help with getting around or with personal care. People with mental health problems are covered by this allowance, even though the application forms are geared towards physical disabilities—it is important not to be put off by this. The disadvantage of DLA is that it is one of the few benefits that cannot be back-dated, so it's a good idea for the individual to apply for it as soon as possible. Disability Living Allowance is not based on National Insurance contributions and can be paid no matter what other benefits, incomes or savings there may be. It does not decrease the amount of other benefits paid, and it is also the gateway to other valuable benefits. The claim pack for Disability Living Allowance is rather complicated, and you and your relative may well need help with claiming (see p. 153). It is particularly advantageous if, as part of their case for receiving DLA, claimants can describe situations or feelings that may handicap them. One of the criteria is whether you are restricted because of mental illness from getting around—so feelings of being persecuted, depression, lack of energy and phobias would all be worth mentioning.

The need for personal care is another criterion for the award of Disability Living Allowance. If your relative does have difficulties maintaining good personal care, it is a good idea when applying to emphasise the fact that this is caused by the impact of severe mental illness. One of the questions that the DLA claim form asks is whether the claimant needs someone to keep an eye on him or her. This covers all sorts of circumstances: for instance, high risk of self-harm, or of setting fire to things by accident. If a claim for DLA is turned down, the individual can seek a review without having to supply any extra evidence, provided he or she writes to the DLA unit within three months of the decision. Even after this, if the claimant is dissatisfied, he or she can seek a special review or appeal.

People who are receiving Income Support as their only benefit, or as their top-up benefit, should get their rent and Council Tax paid in full. However, **Housing Benefit** covers only rent—not water, heating or service charges. The amount of Housing Benefit and the degree of **exemption from Council Tax** can be reduced in certain circumstances where other people live in the claimant's household. The claim has to be renewed every year. People who are not on Income Support but have a low income, or are receiving other benefits, will have some of their rent and Council Tax charges met by benefit if they claim. There is a complicated formula for working out how much should actually be paid. It can take weeks for a claim to be paid, so start early!

Council Tax exemption can in any case be obtained by someone who is 'severely mentally impaired': in this context, this would include severe mental illness. To do this, your relative needs a statement from the doctor. The exemption can be awarded whether the individual is on benefit or not. One good thing about this exemption is that he or she doesn't have to make a new claim every year.

Home owners can get **Council Tax benefit**, provided they are on a low income or receive other benefits. And it is still possible, under certain circumstances, to receive financial help through Income Support to meet mortgage interest payments.

Every year the government allocates a sum of money called the **Social Fund**, administered by the **Benefits Agency**, who can make a grant or loan to people who meet the criteria. In addition to more general grants like maternity expenses, funeral expenses and cold weather payments, they can also provide budgeting loans and crisis loans. You or your relative may be eligible for a budgeting loan if you are in receipt of Income Support at the time of the claim, and have been for the previous twenty-six weeks. However, there are restrictions on what the money can be borrowed for. Moreover, you have to pay it back, and deductions are made from benefit each week until the sum is repaid. In order to obtain a crisis loan it is not necessary to be receiving Income Support, but merely to have 'insufficient resources'. On this basis, for example, your relative might be able to borrow money while awaiting a replacement giro if one has been lost or stolen.

The final sort of payment, which is of particular relevance to people with severe mental illness, is a **Community Care Grant**. This is supposed to promote community care by helping people to move out or stay out of institutional care, or by helping families under exceptional pressure. Once more, the person receiving the grant must be receiving Income Support, and again there is a limit to what the money can be used to pay for. Because people with mental health problems are supposed to be given priority for Community Care Grants, it is essential to make it very clear on the application form that the claimant has such problems and how the money will help him or her to live in the community. A Community Care Grant might be awarded, for instance, to cover clothing or furniture expenses for somebody who is leaving hospital after a long stay. It can also be used to replace expensive items like cookers or fridges. This is particularly the case if some emergency such as a fire or a flood has led to the need to replace the items.

While some people are given a grant at their first application, it is rarely enough to cover what they ask for. Others may be turned down outright, or offered a small grant with the rest as a **top-up loan**. Other people may be offered just a **loan**. However, an unfavourable decision can be reviewed if you request it. It is usually a good idea to get advice from a welfare advice worker when resubmitting a claim, to make sure the claim is as strong as possible. For situations like this, always make a photocopy of the claim form.

If you or your relative is successful in obtaining a loan, it is worth knowing that there are rules about the amount the Benefits Agency should deduct from your benefit each week to repay the loan. If they seem to be taking too much away from you or your relative in repayments, it is always worth seeking advice (see p. 153), because they do make mistakes.

If you or your relative is on Income Support and you have got into arrears with rent, water, gas or electricity, you may find that the Benefits Agency reduces the level of Income Support in order to cover repayments for these debts. This does not actually need the agreement of the claimant, although the Benefits Agency should let him or her know before doing it. Again, if it seems that too much is being taken off, and you and your relative have too little to live on, do seek advice. Some people find that direct deduction of this kind helps them to repay debts and at the same time makes budgeting easier. If this would be of help to you or your relative, you can initiate direct deductions by contacting the Benefits Agency yourselves. Such direct deductions are intended to be available only to those on Income Support, but availability may be extended to people in other circumstances.

In 1995 new tests were introduced to assess incapacity for work. These allow the Benefits Agency to assess whether somebody claiming Income Support, Severe Disability Allowance or Incapacity Benefit is capable of work. After twenty-eight weeks of claiming these benefits, people are assessed for any work under the **all-work test**. If the Benefits Agency knows about your relative's mental health problems, they should not send him or her the questionnaire for assessment of incapacity at this time. People stated by their doctor to be severely mentally ill are exempt from this assessment, and benefits will continue to be paid. If your relative does get a questionnaire, check with the Benefits Agency to see if they have contacted your family doctor.

Most benefits can be back-dated for up to fifty-two weeks, if not claimed at the right time. However, this will happen only if there was a good reason for not claiming at the right time. Ignorance is *not* a good reason! But if ill health prevented a claim being made, or prevented an individual from understanding his or her entitlement, this would be accepted as reason enough.

People with severe mental disorder often go into hospital, and this affects their benefits. Disability Living Allowance and Attendance Allowance (see pp. 148, 153) stop after four weeks in hospital; most other benefits are down-rated after six weeks. People who claim **Incapacity Benefit** have a legal obligation to let the Benefits Agency know when they are admitted to hospital, so that the reductions in benefit can be made at the appropriate time. Most hospitals send in admission certificates to the Benefits Agency, so they are likely to know in any case.

There can be important effects on housing benefits when people are in hospital. Whereas if they are on Income Support they will still have their rent met in full, if they are on Incapacity Benefit, Severe Disablement Allowance or Statutory Sick Pay, and are still in hospital after six weeks, they will find that their housing and Council Tax benefit entitlement is reduced considerably. They are expected to make up the balance from their other benefits, so if they are unaware of this, rent arrears may start to build up.

Every period of home leave from hospital lasting one night or more results in benefit being increased for this period. It is important that the Benefits Agency is told about leave periods, so that payment can be made.

If your relative was working at the time of becoming ill and was earning at least £61 a week, he or she is entitled to Statutory Sick Pay. This is paid by the employers for twenty-eight weeks, but after that the cost is picked up by Incapacity Benefit.

It may be advisable for you to inquire about **Invalid Care Allowance**, which can be paid to a person caring for someone for more than thirty-five hours a week. It does count as income for means-tested benefits, and the person being looked after will then be unable to claim the Severe Disability Premium of Income Support. You would need expert advice as to whether it was a good idea to claim Invalid Care Allowance.

Attendance Allowance is similar to Disability Living Allowance, but applies to people over sixty-five at the time of the claim. It is probably more difficult to qualify for Attendance Allowance than for Disability Living Allowance.

Finally, your relative will almost certainly be eligible for **free prescriptions**. If not, he or she may still be able to save by buying a pre-payment certificate. Under certain circumstances both you and your relative may be entitled to payments to cover travel costs to and from hospital.

In addition to the leaflets available at DSS offices and Post Offices, help with money problems can be obtained from several sources. Most psychiatric hospitals have departments called **Patients' Affairs** or **Welfare Rights**. These are sometimes run by the NHS and sometimes by the local Citizens' Advice Bureau. Usually they deal only with the financial difficulties of **in-patients** and **day patients**, but in some hospitals they may be responsible for out-patients engaged in rehabilitation programmes. They will advise about entitlement to benefits and grants and will manage matters like payment of rent while the patient is in hospital. They are concerned with **statutory benefits**, not with grants from charities and the like. More extensive advice can be had at your local **Citizens' Advice Bureau**.

Out-patients usually have to seek advice about benefits either from social workers or direct from the Citizens' Advice Bureau. Finally, there are various charitable bodies that may be able to help in particular circumstances and for particular purposes. They will often require the recommendation of a doctor.

It is often useful to discuss financial problems with the **social worker** attached to the mental health team, or with one from the local social services department. Social workers will be aware, as well as of benefit entitlement, of other relevant services which, by taking some of the pressures off the family, may help it to maintain its income. Such services may include a home help, a day nursery or play group, and occupation and leisure activities such as day centres, workshops or clubs. A social worker may also visit you at home in order to complete a **needs assessment** form to determine what **you** or **your relative** now requires. If you have not received one, ask your key worker to organise it, or contact social services directly. The social worker will also know of any local organisations offering help to the severely mentally ill or their relatives.

If you have no contact with local authority social workers, it is always worth ringing the local department (the number will be in the phone book under the County or Borough Council). Ask to speak to the social worker on duty. A brief description of your circumstances should be enough to enable the social worker to decide whether it is worth giving you an appointment at the office.

The mental health team involved in the care of your relative are likely to suggest that you get in touch with the hospital social worker, and will explain how to do this.

Appendix 2
Useful Addresses

In this appendix we have listed organisations that may be of use to you or your relative, with a brief account of what they provide. Some are mentioned in more detail in the text, as indicated.

ACCEPT (Alcohol Community Centre for Education, Prevention and Treatment), Accept Clinic, 724 Fulham Road, London SW6 5SE. (0171) 371 7555 (0171) 371 7477 (helpline Mon.–Fri. 9am–5pm)	A treatment centre for people with alcohol problems and their families and friends. A drop-in service is also available.
ADFAM National, 5th Floor, Epworth House, 25 City Road, London EC1Y 1AA. (0171) 638 3700	Supports families and friends of drug users. Runs a national telephone helpline and information service.

Afro-Caribbean Mental Health Association, 35 Electric Avenue, London SW9 8JP. (0171) 737 3603	A community mental health centre which provides a wide range of caring services to the black community, including psychotherapy, counselling and group work. Also provides advice on housing and legal issues concerning mental health, and a volunteer and befriending service.
Al-Anon Family Groups (UK and Eire), 61 Great Dover Street, London SE1 4YF. (0171) 403 0888	Offers help to families of problem drinkers. 24-hour confidential helpline.
Alcoholics Anonymous (AA), General Service Office, PO Box 1, Stonebow House, Stonebow, York YO1 2NJ. (01904) 644026 (office and helpline, Mon.–Fri. 9am–5pm)	A fellowship of men and women who share their experiences to help others recover from alcoholism.
Association for Post-Natal Illness, 25 Jerdan Place, London SW6 1BE. (0171) 386 0868	Advises and supports women suffering from post-natal depression. Runs a network of volunteers to support sufferers throughout the UK. Please write for more information.

Association of Community
Health Councils for England
and Wales,
30 Drayton Park,
London N5 1PB.
(0171) 609 8405

Association of Northern
Ireland District Committees,
25–27 Adelaide Street,
Belfast BT2 8FH.
(01232) 324431

Association of Scottish Local
Health Councils,
18 Alba Street,
Edinburgh EH2 4QG.
(0131) 220 4101

These three organisations officially represent the consumers' interest in the National Health Service. Provide a useful source of information about local mental health facilities. Local branches to be found in the phone directory under 'Community' or the name of the district health authority.

Bristol Crisis Service for
Women,
PO Box 654,
Bristol BS99 1XM.
(0117) 9251119 (office)
(Helpline Fri. and Sat. nights
9pm–12.30am)

British Association for
Counselling,
1 Regent Place,
Warwick Street,
Rugby CV21 2PJ.
(01788) 578328

Supplies names and addresses of qualified counsellors on request. See also Cruse (p. 159), Parents Anonymous (p. 169), Relate (p. 170).

British Medical Association,
BMA House,
Tavistock Square,
London WC1H 9JR.
(0171) 387 4499

The doctors' representative organisation.

British Pregnancy Advisory Service,
Austy Manor,
Wootton Wawen,
Solihull,
West Midlands B95 6BX.
(01564) 793225

Aims primarily to help and advise women faced with an unwanted pregnancy. Additional services include pregnancy testing, contraception, male and female sterilisation and infertility help. Branches throughout the UK.

Brook Advisory Centre,
165 Grays Inn Road,
London WC1X 8UD.
(0171) 713 9000

Offers advice on emotional and sexual problems, contraception. Local branches.

Carers' National Association,
20–25 Glasshouse Yard,
London EC1A 4JS.
(0171) 490 8818

Offers general information from its information department, Mon.–Fri., office hours. Carers' adviser available to give more in-depth telephone advice, Mon.–Fri. 1pm–4pm, (0171) 490 8898.

Carr-Gomm Society Ltd,
6 Tabard Street,
London SE1 4JU.
(0171) 397 5300

Runs hostels for the lonely and single.

Centrepoint,
Bewlay House,
2 Swallow Place,
London W1R 7AA.
(0171) 629 2229 (office)
(0171) 287 9134 (24-hour helpline)

Organises twelve homes, including two overnight emergency shelters for young adults aged 16–25.

Charities Aid Foundation,
Kings Hill,
West Malling,
Kent ME19 4TA.
(01732) 520000

CITA (Council for Involuntary Tranquilliser Addiction),
Cavendish House,
Brighton Road,
Waterloo,
Liverpool L22 5NG.
(0151) 949 0102

Offers advice and support to people wishing to withdraw from tranquillisers and antidepressants. Helpline.

Court of Protection,
24 Kingsway,
London WC2 6JX.
(0171) 664 7000

See p. 57.

Cruse Bereavement Care,
Cruse House,
126 Sheen Road,
Richmond,
Surrey TW9 1UR.
(0171) 940 4818 (office)
(0181) 332 7227 (bereavement counsellor)

Offers counselling, advise and opportunities for social contact to all bereaved people. Office hours, Mon.–Fri.

Depression Alliance,
(formerly Depressives Associated),
PO Box 1022,
London SE1 7QB.
(0171) 721 7672

Provides information, support and understanding for people who suffer from depression and the problems associated with it.

Depressives Anonymous, 36 Chestnut Avenue, Beverley, North Humberside HU17 9QU. (01482) 860619 (answerphone after office hours)	Offers general advice and information and support, office hours.
Disablement Income Group, 19 Wedmore Street, London N19 4RZ. (0171) 263 3981	Advises on financial problems, benefits and allowances. Local branches.
Drinkline, National Alcohol Helpline, Weddel House, 7th Floor, 13–14 West Smithfield, London EC1A 9DL. (0171) 332 0150 (office) (0171) 332 0202 (helpline 6pm–11pm 7 days a week)	Offers confidential information, help and advice for sufferers, friends and relatives.
Drugline Ltd, 9A Brockley Cross, Brockley, London SE4 2AB. (0181) 692 4975	Offers confidential advice and counselling on drug-related problems.
Ex-Services Mental Welfare Society, Broadway House, The Broadway, London SW19 1RL. (0181) 543 6333	May provide charitable funds for eligible mentally ill people in financial difficulty.

Families Anonymous,
Room 8,
650 Holloway Road,
London N19 3NU.
(0171) 498 4680 (1–4.30pm; 24-hour answerphone at other times)

Helps families and friends of drug users through local self-help groups. Completely anonymous and independent.

Family Service Units,
207 Old Marylebone Road,
London NW1 5QP.
(0171) 402 5175
See local phone directory.

Provides support and services for couples with young children. Casework.

Family Welfare Association,
501 Kingsland Road,
London E8 4AU.
(0171) 254 6251

Voluntary social work to families. Publishes *Charities Digest* and a guide to the social services.

General Medical Council,
178–202 Great Portland Street,
London W1N 6JE.
(0171) 580 7642

Monitors the medical profession's standards of service and behaviour.

Good Practice in Mental Health,
380–384 Harrow Road,
London W9 2HU.
(0171) 289 2034

Promotes and assists the development of good mental health services by disseminating information, to people working in the mental health field, about local services via an information service, consultancy and developmental support and conferences. Self-advocacy team works with mental health and self-advocacy groups across London.

Holiday Care Service, 2nd Floor, Imperial Building, Victoria Road, Horley, Surrey RH6 7PZ. (01293) 774535	Provides information for people with special holiday needs, including the mentally ill.
Institute for the Study of Drug Dependence, 1 Hatton Place, Hatton Garden, London EC1N 8ND. (0171) 430 1991	Disseminates information and promotes research on all aspects of drug misuse, to advance public understanding. Information service available.
International Stress Management Association, South Bank University, LPSS, 103 Borough Road, London SE1 0AA.	Offers a mailing address for people to write to for information on where to get help and self-help material for improving stress-management skills.
Jewish Association for the Mentally Ill, 707 High Road, Finchley, London N12 0BT. (0181) 343 1111	Provides help and advice to sufferers and their carers. Runs a day club once a week and aims to provide a team of volunteer befrienders.
Jewish Care, 221 Golders Green Road, London NW11 9DQ. (0181) 458 3282	Runs hostels.
Jewish Marriage Council, 23 Ravenshurst Avenue, London NW4 4EL. (0181) 203 6311	Offers marital counselling to people of any or no denomination.

Leonard Cheshire Foundation,
26–29 Maunsell Street,
London SW1P 2QN.
(0171) 828 1822

Runs hostels and offers domiciliary support for mentally handicapped and psychiatric patients.

Liberty (formerly National Council for Civil Liberties),
21 Tabard Street,
London SE1 4LA.
(0171) 403 3888

Manic Depression Fellowship,
98–100 High Street,
Kingston-upon-Thames,
Surrey KT1 1EY.
(0181) 974 6550

Telephone advice available Mon.–Fri. 9am–5pm. Answerphone outside of these hours; they will always ring back when the office is next open if you leave a message. Network of local groups. See p. 123.

Marriage Care (Catholic Marriage Advisory Council),
46 Notting Hill Gate,
London W11 3HZ.
(0171) 243 1898

Offers marital counselling to people of any or no denomination.

Mental After-Care Association (MACA),
25 Bedford Square,
London WC1B 3HW.
(0171) 436 6194

Provides residential services for people recovering from mental illness and information on services run by other organisations around the country. Also runs employment and respite schemes and does court liaison work for mentally disordered offenders.

Mental Health Act Commission, Maid Marian House, 56 Houndsgate, Nottingham NG1 6RG. (0115) 943 7100 Mental Health Act Commission for Northern Ireland, Elizabeth House, 118 Holywood Road, Belfast BT4 1NY. (01232) 651157	See pp. 135, 137.
Mental Health Foundation, 37 Mortimer Street, London W1N 8JU. (0171) 580 0145	Provides general information, various booklets. Funds research in mental health and innovative projects to help the mentally ill, especially in the community.
Mental Health Media Council, 356 Holloway Road, London N7 6PA. (0171) 700 8129	Aims to improve the provision and use of appropriate media in mental health education; to act as intermediary between organisations and individuals working in mental health and professionals who produce audio-visual material; to advise writers on mental health topics, and mental health workers on the media.

Mental Health Review Tribunals, 3rd Floor, Cressington House, 249 St Mary's Road, Garston, Liverpool L19 0NF. (0151) 494 0095 Mental Health Review Tribunals, 4th Floor, New Crown Buildings, Cathays Park, Cardiff CF1 3NQ (01222) 825328 Mental Health Review Tribunals, Mental Health Branch, Room 3C, Dundonald House, Stormont Estate, Belfast BT4 3FF (01232 485550)	See p. 131.
Mental Welfare Commission for Scotland, K Floor, Argyle House, 3 Lady Lawson Street, Edinburgh EH3 9SH. (0131) 222 6111	The Scottish equivalent of the Mental Health Act Commission.

MIND (National Association for Mental Health),
Granta House,
15–19 The Broadway,
Stratford,
London E15 4BQ.
(0181) 519 2122

Works for and supports people experiencing mental distress, and their families and carers. National office information department operates Mon.–Fri., 10am–12.30pm and 2pm–4.30pm. Staff at the national office's legal department have specific legal training and offer information and advice, Mon., Wed. and Fri., 2–4.30pm. MIND publishes clear and concise leaflets on legal rights. A network of local support groups offers friendship and mutual support to people with mental health problems. For information on local groups, contact your nearest regional office from the list below.

MIND North West,
21 Ribblesdale Place,
Preston,
Lancashire PR1 3NA.
(01772) 821734

MIND Northern,
158 Durham Road,
Gateshead NE8 4EL.
(0191) 490 0109

MIND South East,
Kemp House,
First Floor,
152–160 City Road,
London EC1 2NP.
(0171) 608 0881

MIND South West,
9th Floor,
Tower House,
Fairfax Street,
Bristol BS1 3BN.
(0117) 925 0960

MIND Trent & Yorkshire,
The White Building,
Fitzalan Square,
Sheffield S1 2AY
(0114) 272 1742

MIND Wales,
23 St Mary Street,
Cardiff CF1 2AA.
(01222) 395123

MIND West Midlands,
20–21 Cleveland Street,
Wolverhampton WV1 3HT.
(01902) 24404

National Association of
Voluntary Hostels,
33 Long Acre,
London WC2E 9LA.
(0171) 240 3222

Useful source of information about national availability of hostels.

National Schizophrenia
Fellowship,
28 Castle Street,
Kingston-upon-Thames,
Surrey KT6 4NS.
(0181) 547 3937 (office)
(0181) 974 6814 (advice line)

National Schizophrenia
Fellowship (Northern Ireland),
Windhurst,
Knochbrachen Health Care
Park,
Saintfield Road,
Belfast BT8 8BH.
(01232) 248006

National Schizophrenia
Fellowship (Scotland),
40 Shandwick Place,
Edinburgh EH2 4RT.
(0131) 226 2025

Offer advice, support and information to people suffering from schizophrenia, their families and carers. See p. 122.

National Self-Help Support Networks, c/o National Self-Help Support Centre, NCVO, Regents Wharf, 8 All Saints Street, London N1 9RL. (0171) 713 6161	Assists in setting up self-help groups wherever there is a shared experience. Coordinates national network meetings of self-help support staff to share information and experience and discuss current issues; answers inquiries about self-help and produces information sheets; maintains a database of self-help activity; organises training courses and develops training materials aimed at self-help groups and those who work with them.
Northern Ireland Association for Mental Health, 80 University Street, Belfast BT7 1AH. (01232) 328474	
NSPCC, 67 Saffron Hill, London EC1N 8RS. (0800) 800 500 (a 24-hour freephone number)	Child protection helpline, staffed by qualified counsellors, both male and female.
Office of Care and Protection, Royal Courts of Justice, Chichester Street, Belfast BT1 3JF. (01232) 235111	Northern Irish equivalent of the English Court of Protection.

Office of Parliamentary Commissioners and Health Service Commissioners for England,
Church House,
Great Smith Street,
London SW1P 3BW.
(0171) 217 4051

Health Service Commissioner for Scotland,
Ground Floor,
1 Athol Place,
Edinburgh EH3 8HP.
(0131) 225 7465

Health Service Commissioner for Wales,
4th Floor Pearl Assurance House,
Greyfriars Road,
Cardiff CF1 3AG.
(01222) 394621

The health 'Ombudsmen'. If you are dissatisfied with the way a complaint has been handled by the hospital authorities, you can take it to the Health Service Commissioner. The Northern Irish equivalent is the Commissioner for Complaints.

Parents Anonymous,
Manor Gardens Centre,
8 Manor Gardens,
Islington,
London N7 6LA.
(0171) 263 8918

Offers friendship and help to parents who are at risk of abusing their children and to those who may have done so. Telephone counselling and visiting service. Network of local groups.

Patients Association,
Union House,
8 Guilford Street,
London WC1N 1DT.
(0171) 242 3460

Independent pressure group for patients. Offers advice and information.

Philadelphia Association,
4 Marty's Yard,
17 Hampstead High Street,
London NW3 1PX.
(0171) 794 2652

Aims to relieve mental distress through low-cost residential therapeutic communities and private psychotherapy service.

Psychiatric Rehabilitation Association,
Bayford Mews,
Bayford Street,
London E8 3SF.
(0181) 985 3570

Aims to promote the rehabilitation of the mentally sick on their return home to employment and society by preparatory work (including evening and day centres, shop work experience courses and industrial education) in the community; and to promote practical measures in research for the prevention and combating of mental stress within the community.

Rape Crisis Centre,
PO Box 69,
London WC1X 9NJ.
(0171) 278 3956 (office)
(0171) 837 1600 (24-hour helpline)

A 24-hour helpline run by women for women and girls who have been raped or sexually assaulted.

Relate (Marriage Guidance Council).
See local phone directory.

Trained volunteers offer counselling and practical advice; book lists and books. Those who can afford it may be asked to contribute to costs.

Relate: National Marriage Guidance,
Herbert Gray College,
Little Church Street,
Rugby,
Warwicks CV21 3AP.
(01788) 573241

Gives details of local counselling services for those seeking help with marriage/family relationships and sexual problems. Mon.–Fri., office hours.

Release,
388 Old Street,
London EC1V 9LT.
(0171) 729 5255 (office)
(0171) 729 9904 (advice line, 10am–6pm)
(0171) 603 8654 (overnight emergency helpline)

Gives legal or drugs advice on the telephone, plus appropriate referral if needed. Offers support to all callers, and aims for harm minimisation.

Remploy Ltd,
415 Edgware Road,
London NW2 6LR.
(0181) 235 0500.

Provides sheltered employment. Candidates selected by Disablement Resettlement Officer.

Richmond Fellowship,
8 Addison Road,
London W14 8DL.
(0171) 603 6373

Provides care and rehabilitation for people who have experienced problems with mental health or substance abuse. Runs long- and short-stay residential facilities, work schemes, day centres, advocacy and community outreach projects.

Royal College of Psychiatrists,
17 Belgrave Square,
London SW1X 8PG.
(0171) 235 2351

Representative organisation of psychiatrists in the UK. Sets training standards.

SAD Association,
PO Box 969,
London SW7 9PZ.
(01604) 846070

SAD (Seasonal Affective Disorder) is the depressive winter illness that can so badly affect sufferers that they cannot function in winter without medical treatment. Offers information and advice and refers people to specialist SAD clinics. Hires out light-boxes for people to try out the treatment in the comfort of their own home.

Sainsbury's Centre for Mental Health (formerly RDP), 134–138 Borough High Street, London SE1 1LB. (0171) 403 8790	Aims to improve the quality of life of people with severe and long-term mental health problems through detailed research, plus national programmes and training, conferences, publications and an information service.
Samaritans. (0345) 909090 See local phone directory.	Offers advice, support and befriending by phone to the despairing, or those worried by someone who is.
SANE, 2nd Floor, Worthington House, 199–205 Old Marylebone Road, London NW1 5QP. (0171) 724 6570 (office) (0171) 724 8000 (helpline Fri. 6pm–2am, Sat. 2pm–2am, Sun. 2pm–2am, Bank Holidays 2pm–2am) (0345) 678000 (national helpline)	Helplines providing information and support on schizophrenia and other mental health problems.
Schizophrenia Association of Great Britain, Bryn Hyfryd, The Crescent, Bangor, Gwynedd LL57 2AG. (01248) 354048	Offers advice and information by phone or letter. Has a primarily 'biological' view of schizophrenia.

Scottish Association for Mental Health,
17a Graham Street,
Edinburgh EH6 5QN.
(0131) 229 9687

The Scottish MIND.
See p. 166.

Shelter.
Freephone (0800) 446 441
(6pm–9am)

Gives advice and referrals to anyone experiencing housing problems in London.

Simon Community,
PO Box 1187,
London NW5 4HW.
(0171) 485 6639

Helps ex-psychiatric patients, among others, to find accommodation.

Survivors Speak,
34 Osnaburgh Street,
London NW1 3ND.
(0171) 916 5472/3

Run by former sufferers of mental illness, aims to improve communication and contact between users and ex-users of psychiatric services. Publishes advocacy packs and regularly organises conferences and reports. Aims to provide an information database accessible to survivors all over Britain.

Terrence Higgins Trust,
52–54 Gray's Inn Road,
London WC1X 8JU
(0171) 831 0330 (office)
(0171) 242 1010 (helpline, 12–10pm daily)
(0171) 405 2381 (legal line, Wed. 7–9pm)

Aims to provide welfare, legal and counselling help and support to people with AIDS and related conditions, and to their friends and families; to disseminate accurate information about AIDS; to provide health education for those at risk.

Turning Point,
New Loom House,
101 Backchurch Lane,
London E1 1LU.
(0171) 702 2300

National charity helping people with drink, drug and mental health problems. Provides rehabilitation, day care and street-level advice, and a counselling service for people seeking help.

UK Advocacy Network,
Premier House,
14 Cross Burgess Street,
Sheffield S1 2MG
(0114) 272 8171

Campaigns for patients' councils, advocacy projects and user forums which are involved in planning and working for change in the mental health system.

Victims' Helpline,
St Leonard's House,
Nuttall Street,
London N1 5LZ.
(0171) 729 1226 (office)
(0171) 729 1252 (helpline)

Offers a 24-hour confidential helpline for victims of any crime and their families; provides telephone counselling, information and referral service.

Volunteer Centre,
29 Lower King's Road,
Berkhamsted,
Herts HP4 2AB
(01442) 873311

Provides information about local voluntary facilities.

Women's Aid Federation.
Helpline (0345) 023468

Provides accommodation and support for battered wives.

Women's Royal Voluntary Service,
Milton Hill House,
Milton Hill,
Abingdon,
Oxon OX13 6AF.
(01235) 442900

Provides meals on wheels.

Women's Therapy Centre,
6–9 Manor Gardens,
London N7 6LA.
(0171) 263 6200 (Mon.–Fri.
1.30pm–4.00pm)

Provides individual and group psychotherapy for women.

Zito Trust,
PO Box 265,
London WC2H 9JD.
(0171) 240 8422

Established to work for improvements in the provision of community care for the severely mentally ill, to support the victims of the failure of care and to carry out research and training in this field.

Index

AA (Alcoholics Anonymous) 156
ACCEPT 155
Access to Health Records Act (1990) 72
accommodation/housing 67, 84–6
  private providers 68–9
addiction
  substance abuse 45
  to benzodiazepines 109, 111
ADFAM National 155
admission to hospital 95–6
  effects on benefits 152
  emergency 47–52, 127–8
affective illness 11
Afro-Caribbean Mental Health Association 156
agitated behaviour 21
Al-Anon 156
alcohol 44–5
  medication and 44, 106
Alcoholics Anonymous 156
all-work test 152
allergies and mental illness 20
alternative therapies 123
amitriptyline 97, 105
amphetamines 45
antidepressants 104–9
anxiety states 40
Association for Post-Natal Illness 156
ASWs (Approved Social Workers) 78
Attendance Allowance 153
attitudes towards mental illness 6
auditory hallucinations 24–5
  case report 8–9

bathing/washing 43
'befrienders' 68
behaviour therapy 19, 120–1
benefit system 147–54
benzodiazepines 109–11
birth/post-partum mental illness 17–18, 82
blood tests 82
  clozapine monitoring 102–4
  lithium monitoring 108
booklets/publications 146
brain chemistry 6, 17
  antidepressants and 105–6
  ECT effects 112
brain damage/injury 16
brain scans 82
brain surgery 114–15
Bristol Crisis Service for Women 157
British Association for Counselling 157
British Medical Association 157
British Pregnancy Advisory Service 158
Brook Advisory Centre 158
budgeting loans 150

cancer fears 22, 24
cannabis 45
carbamazepine 109
care plan 65
Care Programme Approach 3, 64, 65–7
  key workers 47, 65
Care Programme Register 73
Carers' National Association 158

Carr-Gomm Society 158
catatonic stupor 113
causes of mental illness 15–20
CBT (cognitive behaviour therapy) 19, 120–1
Centrepoint 158
Charities Aid Foundation 159
chemical imbalance theory 6, 17
  antidepressants and 105–6
  ECT and 112
childhood experiences 19–20
children of patient 58–60
CITA 159
Citizen's Advice Bureau 153
clinical psychologists 78–80, 120–1
clozapine (Clozaril) 102–4
Clunís, Christopher 27, 68
cocaine 45
cognitive therapy 19, 120–1
community care 63–73
Community Care Act (1992) 31, 84
Community Care Grant 150–1
community mental health teams 76
  psychiatric nurses 47, 77
Community Supervision Orders 4
complaints procedures 136–7, 169
compulsory admission/sectioning 47, 93, 95, 124–34
compulsory treatment 134–6
computerised records 71–2
confidentiality issues 70–2
  Supervision Register 73
constipation 22
consultant psychiatrists *see* psychiatrists
'continuity of care' principle 3, 65
contracts (legal) 137–8
coping with mental illness 31–62
  carer's needs 140–6
  depression 35–8
  emergencies 46–52
cortisol 18
Council Tax 149–50
counselling 121
  British Association 157
Court of Protection 57–8, 159
CPA *see* Care Programme Approach
CPNs (community psychiatric nurses) 47, 77
'crack' 45
crime/petty crime 69
criminal justice system 69
crisis intervention centres 48–9
crisis loans 150
Cruse Bereavement Care 159
cyclothymic personality 18

Data Protection Act (1984) 71
day centres 87
delusions 8, 24, 27
  coping with 38–40
  loss of insight and 28–9
  of persecution 27
Depression Alliance 159
depressive illness 11
  causes 18–20
  coping with 35–8, 40
  depressive neurosis 11–12
  depressive psychosis 11
  drug treatment 104–11
  ECT for 112–14
  effect on sexual relationships 40–1
  onset (case reports) 12–14
  post-partum 18
  relapse signs 61
  social/psychological treatments 115–23
  see also manic depressive illness
Depressives Anonymous 160
detained patients/compulsory admission 47, 93, 95, 124–34
diazepam 97
diet 42–3
  MAOIs and 106, 107
  mental illness due to? 20, 42
Disability Living Allowance 148–9
Disablement Income Group 160
Disablement Resettlement Officer (DRO) 88, 146
discharge from hospital 84
  against medical advice 125
disordered speech 26
District Health Authorities (DHAs) 67

divorce 41, 138
DLA (Disability Living Allowance) 148–9
doctors
  clinical psychologists 78–80, 120–1
  family doctors 67–8, 81, 92, 93, 127–8
  psychiatrists 74–6, 81–2, 84
  second opinions 92–3
  in training 75
domestic tensions 20
domiciliary visits 48, 81
dopamine theory 17
Drinkline 160
driving (legal aspects) 138–9
DRO (Disablement Resettlement Officer) 88, 146
drug abuse 45
drug overdose 49–52
drug treatment 96–112
  alcohol and 44, 106
  compulsory 134–6
  driving and 138–9
  prescription costs 153
  problems taking 62, 109, 111–12
  side effects 43, 100–11
Drugline 160

Ecstasy (E) 45
ECT (electroconvulsive therapy) 112–14, 134
embarrassing behaviour 34–5
emergencies 46–52
  emergency admission 47–52, 127–8
  suicide attempts 49–52
  violent behaviour 55–6
emotional responses (loss of) 23, 33
employment aspects 87–8
  all-work test 152
  Disablement Resettlement Officer 88, 146
  sheltered workshops 117–18
  Statutory Sick Pay 152
encephalitis lethargica 16
endocrine disorders 16
energy loss/inertia 32, 34
Ex-Services Mental Welfare Society 160
extra contractual referrals 93

facial expression 23, 33, 100
Families Anonymous 161
family doctors (GPs) 67–8, 81
  emergency admissions and 127–8
  second-opinion referrals 92, 93
Family Service Units 161
family therapy 121–2
Family Welfare Association 161
financial aspects
  benefit system 147–54
  money problems (of patient) 56–8
  social service budgets 66
First Aid in Mental Health (Melville) 146

General Medical Council 161
general paresis of the insane 16
genetic aspects 15–16, 59–60
genetic counselling 60
glutamine theory 17
Good Practice in Mental Health 161
GPI (general paresis of the insane) 16
GPs (family doctors) 67–8, 81
  emergency admissions and 127–8
  second-opinion referrals 92, 93
grimacing 100
group homes 85
group therapy 118–19
guilt feelings in depression 24

hallucinations 8, 25
  auditory 24–5
health insurance 93
health preoccupations 22
health professionals
  dealing with 88–93
  see also doctors; nurses; social workers
health record access 72
hearing voices 24–5
heroin abuse 45
holidays/social activities 36, 144
  carers' needs 141, 144

Holiday Care Service 162
home/domiciliary visits 48, 81
hormonal state 17–18
hospital care 95–6, 124
  catchment areas 48, 92
  complaints procedures 94
  compulsory admission/sectioning 47, 93, 95, 124–34
  day hospital 86
  discharge from 84, 125
  effects on benefits 152
  emergency admission 47–52, 127–8
  length of stay 31
  psychiatric wards 82–4
  teaching hospitals 92
  to reduce suicide risk 46
hostels 84–5
Housing Benefit 149
housing needs 67, 84–6
  private providers 68–9
hypomania 23
  hypomanic personality 18–19
hysterical split personality 7

in-patient care *see* hospital care
Incapacity (Sickness) Benefit 147, 148, 151
Income Support 148, 151
indecisiveness 37
inertia/laziness 32, 34
infective causes of mental illness 16
inheritance of mental illness 15–16, 59–60
Institute for the Study of Drug Dependence 162
International Stress Management Association 162
Invalid Care Allowance 153

Jewish Association for the Mentally Ill 162
Jewish Care 162
Jewish Marriage Council 162
jobs *see* employment aspects
jury service 138

key workers 47, 65, 74

Laing, R.D. 19
laziness/inertia 32, 34
legal aspects 124–39
  compulsory admission 124–34
  confidentiality 70–2
  Court of Protection 57–8
  dismissal from work 88
  petty crime/court appearances 69
  power of attorney 57
  Section 117 requirements 66, 84
Leonard Cheshire Foundation 163
letters/mail 136
leucotomy 114–15
Liberty 163
lithium 108
loans 150
lobotomy 114–15
Lord Chancellor's Visitors 58
LSD 45

MACA (Mental After-Care Association) 86, 163
mail/post 136
major tranquillisers 98–104
manager's hearing 129
Manerix (moclobemide) 104, 106
Manic Depression Fellowship 93, 123, 163
manic depressive illness 10–15
  causes 15–20
  cognitive therapy for 121
  coping with 31–62
  drug treatment 98, 108, 109
  ECT for 112
  genetic aspects 59–60
  money problems 56–7
  onset (case report) 13–14
  outlook 29–30
  relapse signs 60–2
  schizoaffective disorder 15
  symptoms 20–9
MAOIs 104–7
marriage breakdown 41, 138
Marriage Care 163
Maudsley Hospital (London) 48–9
medication *see* drug treatment
menopause 17

Mental After-Care Association 86, 163
Mental Health Act (1983) 49, 66, 125
 Section 117 requirement 66, 84
 compulsory admission 47, 49, 93, 95, 124–34
Mental Health Act Commission 135, 164
 complaints to 136–7
Mental Health (Patients in the Community) Act (1995) 3, 31–2, 128
 supervised discharge 135–6
Mental Health Foundation 146, 164
Mental Health Media Council 164
Mental Health Review Tribunals 131–4, 165
mental hospitals 82, 153
 see also hospital care
Mental Welfare Commission (Scotland) 137, 165
MHRT (Mental Health Review Tribunal) 131–4, 165
MIND 146, 166–7
 legal advice department 88, 131
 Tribunal booklet 134
minor tranquillisers 98, 109
moclobemide (Manerix) 104, 106
money problems (of patient) 56–8
monoamine oxidase inhibitors 104–7
murderous behaviour 27–8
myths about mental illness 6

National Association of Voluntary Hostels 167
National Schizophrenia Fellowship 122–3, 167
 publications 146
National Self-Help Support Networks 168
needs assessment 65, 83
negative symptoms 28, 116
 in manic depressive illness 15
 in schizophrenia 9–10, 30
 treatment of 98
neurotransmitter theories 17
NHS reforms 67–8
NHS Trusts 67
Northern Ireland 137
Northern Ireland Association for Mental Health 168
NSPCC 168
nurses 77
 community psychiatric 47
nutrition *see* diet

occupational therapy 80, 116–17
Office of Care and Protection 168
olanzapine (Zyprexa) 103
Ombudsmen 169
OT (occupational therapy) 80, 116–17
overdose emergencies 49–52

paracetamol overdose 49–52
Parents Anonymous 169
Parkinsonism (drug-induced) 100
Patients Association 169
Patients' Charter 70
persecution beliefs 24
personal hygiene 43
personality types/disorders 18–19
Philadelphia Association 170
place of safety order 49, 127
poisoning 49–52
police 49, 55
 place of safety order 127
post-natal mental problems 17–18, 83
 Association for Post-Natal Illness 156
post/mail 136
power of attorney 57
prescription costs 153
private providers
 hospital care 82–3
 housing needs 68–9
 psychiatric treatment 93
promiscuous behaviour 41–2
protection of information 70–2
Prozac 104
Psychiatric Rehabilitation Association 86, 87, 170

psychiatric services/hospitals 68–9, 81–4, 153
psychiatrists 74–6, 81–2, 84, 120–1
  private doctors 93
  referral to/home visits 81
  second opinions 92–3
psychoanalysis 119–20
psychologists (clinical) 78–80, 120–1
psychosurgery 114–15
psychotherapy 119–20
purchaser/provider split 67–8

Rape Crisis Centre 170
Receiver (Court of Protection) 57, 58
recovery position 50–2
Registered Mental Nurses 77
rehabilitation services 86–8
relapses 60–2
  depressive illness 15
  emergencies 46–52
  promiscuity as sign of 42
  violence as sign of 56
Relate 170
relationships
  breakdown of 137–8
  sexual 40–1
Release 171
Remploy 87, 171
rented accommodation 85
Responsible Medical Officers 73, 129
Richmond Fellowship 86, 87, 171
risperidone (Risperdol) 103, 104
RMNs (Registered Mental Nurses) 77
RMOs (Responsible Medical Officers) 73, 129
Royal College of Psychiatrists 171

SAD Association 171–2
Sainsbury's Centre for Mental Health 172
Samaritans 172
SANE 172
schizoaffective disorder 15
schizophrenia 7–10
  causes 15–20
  cognitive therapy for 121
  coping with 31–62
  drug treatment 98–104
  ECT and 113
  genetic aspects 59
  outlook 30
  relapse signs 61
  schizoaffective disorder 15
  symptoms 8–10, 20–9
Schizophrenia Association 172
Scotland 137
Scottish Association for Mental Health 173
seasonal affective disorder (SAD) 171–2
second opinions 92–3
Section 117 requirement 66, 84
sectioning/compulsory admission 47, 93, 95, 124–34
selective serotonin reuptake inhibitors 104
self-care 43
self-help groups 91–2, 122
  National Schizophrenia Fellowship 122, 167
  Someone to Talk to Directory 146
  useful addresses 155–75
self-poisoning 49–52
serotonin uptake inhibitors 104, 106
sertindole (Serdolect) 103
Severe Disablement Allowance 148
sex hormones 17
sexual relationships 40–1
  promiscuous behaviour 41–2
Shelter 173
sheltered accommodation 85–6
sheltered workshops 117–18
shock treatment (ECT) 112–14
Sickness Benefit *see* Incapacity Benefit
side-effects of medication 43, 100–11
Simon Community 173
sleep disturbances 21–2
  inertia 34
  in manic states 22, 23, 61–2

social activities 36, 144
  carers' needs 141, 144
social services 64, 78
social workers 77–8, 90, 153–4
  emergency admissions and 127–8
specialist psychiatric services 68–9
speech (disordered) 26
split personality 7
SRNs (State Registered Nurses) 77
SSRIs 104, 106
State Registered Nurses 77
Statutory Sick Pay 152
stigma of mental illness 6
stress hormones 18
substance abuse 45
suicide/suicide threats 21, 45–6
  compulsory admission 126
  emergency care 49–52
  Supervision Registers 72
supervised discharge 135–6
Supervision Registers 72–3
Survivors Speak 173
swearing 34–5
symptoms 8–10, 20–9
  after-effects of illness 32–4
  of relapse 60–2
syphilis 16

talking therapies 119–22
tardive dyskinesia 100
teaching hospitals 92
Terrence Higgins Trust 173
tiredness 32–4
tranquillizers 98–104
  alcohol and 44
treatment
  prognosis and 29–30
  social/psychological 115–23
  see also drug treatment
tribunals 131–4, 165
Tryptizol (amitriptyline) 97, 105
Turning Point 174
twin studies 15–16

UK Advocacy Network 174
Understanding Mental Health (Gibbs) 146
unpredictable behaviour 33–4

Valium (diazepam) 97
venereal disease fears 22, 24
Victims' Helpline 174
violent behaviour 26–8
  coping with 52–6
  removal from GP'ss list 68
viral theories 16
vitamin deficiencies 42
Volunteer Centre 174
voting rights 138

ward managers 77
washing/bathing 43
wills 137–8
Women's Aid Federation 174
Women's Royal Voluntary Service 174
Women's Therapy Centre 175
work *see* employment aspects
workshops (sheltered) 117–18

Zito, Jonathan 27
Zito Trust 175
Zyprexa (olanzapine) 103